10.

HAM & PIGS

BY THE SAME AUTHOR

Pulling Punches
Farming Times
George Soper's Horses

PAUL HEINEY

HAM & PIGS

A Celebration of the Whole Hog

EXCELLENT PRESS
London
1995

First published 1995 by
Excellent Press, 103 Lonsdale Road
Barnes, London SW13 9DA

Illustrated with wood engravings
by Ian Stephens

ISBN 1 854 87 2842

Printed in Great Britain by
Cromwell Press

To Alice
The First and the Best

Acknowledgements

Most of the people I interviewed for this book are rarely in the spotlight. The trades of butcher, slaughtermen and ham-curer have little obvious glamour and the tasks they perform to put food on our plates are ones on which most would rather not dwell. I am grateful to them all for stepping out from the shadows and sharing the secrets of their trade with me.

During the writing of the book, I was often asked what my current project was and I managed, through practice, to condense the reply to: I am writing a book about pigs and ham. This tended to prevent any further questions. There were many who doubted whether an entire book could be devoted to such a subject but I had no doubts, and I am grateful to David Burnett for the confidence he showed in commissioning the book.

I must also thank, in particular, my local butchers, Jeremy Thickett and Charlie Mills of Bramfield Slaughterers, Cutters and Curers who have been patient beyond the call of duty during the time I have been keeping pigs, and offered advice and met all requests for help and information with enthusiasm. I am also grateful to them for the many yards of sausage skin they seem to have supplied at no charge.

My introduction to Romi and Angela Boueriu in Salonta, Romania, was made by Sue Thompson, and as a result I was able to step back into a pig-keeping culture which is still alive in Eastern Europe but is now extinct in Britain. Romi and Angela devoted many hours and much precious money to ensuring I saw as much of the Romanian way of life as was possible in seven short days.

I must thank my family who have suffered much. Nicholas and Rose have bravely had to face a plate of cooked pig's ears in the course of the writing of this book, along with all manner of bizarre puddings and sausages from around Britain. This they have done bravely and with good humour. My wife Libby has also borne a great burden but has shown great fortitude and faced all crises as well as could be expected of even a seasoned farmer's wife. But she would not taste the pigs' ears.

I must also thank our small breeding herd of Large Black pigs; Alice, Polly, the departed Phoebe and Thora, and the boar Murphy. It has not always been easy keeping them in order, but somehow I feel honoured that they have let me tend them.

Introduction

I have one vivid memory of my childhood. It is not one of the great tableaux of family life; of Christmas, seaside holidays or family feasts, but it was etched on my childish brain to such a depth that whenever hungry thoughts cross my mind, this picture recurs. It is of no more than a ramshackle wooden hut, half-hidden in a wood, on the roadside between Doncaster and Bridlington.

As a child, I travelled this road most summer weekends on slow car journeys in Austin Sevens which had all the facilities that motor cars of that time offered, but not necessarily available all at the same time. For instance, I remember one of these journeys through thick fog, at night, in Doncaster. The headlights opted to be unavailable. Grandfather, in the manner of the luckless squaddie of the platoon, was ordered out of the car by my grandmother and told to walk in front to warn others that we were coming, and also to show us the way. He must have trudged many miles, like the man who waved the red flag to announce the coming of Stevenson's *Rocket*, for as I drifted in and out of what seemed like many hours sleep he was still there; a ghostly, hunched figure with a walking stick, of such an age that he really should not have been out at that time of night, let alone hobbling in front of a spluttering Austin looking for the A1. But all credit to him. Without so much as a hesitation he guided us safely into the car park of the Doncaster General Hospital. The only pity was that he thought we were on the main road home to Sheffield.

But on clear summer days we would speed along these roads at an exhilarating 28 miles an hour, flashing through Hooten Roberts, Rawlcliffe and Goole. And somewhere along this road was this hut. It was hardly a distinguished building; it was built of wood, painted green and had various ad-hoc additions all lacking any element of perpendicularity. But on a peeling blackboard that lay on the verge, it offered an invitation and it was my abiding childhood dream that one day I would be able to take advantage of it.

The sign, scribbled in chalk, said simply "Ham and Eggs". No more than that. Every time we saw it, there was a collective licking of the family lips and "Oh, ah, I could just fancy . . ." but there was always an

7

excuse to press on, or look for somewhere else to stop, or wait till we had filled up with petrol, or found a pub for Dad to tank-up. I learned from an early age that some things are going to be perpetually out of one's reach, no matter how long one may live. "Ham and eggs" was to be at the top of my list.

One day, we did stop at the little green hut and it turned out to be far removed from the secret land flowing with milk, honey, eggs and ham that I had fondly imagined it to be. It stank of cats, and had rusty iron garden chairs round tables covered with lino (which was possibly where the stench of cat piddle was coming from). But, trying my hardest to ignore the miserable environment, I thought that at last my dream was about to come true. But no. On the grounds of economy I was confined to a miserable poached egg on toast with a yolk baked as hard as a bullet. Ham and eggs remained as elusive as if we had sped past the green hut at our usual spluttering crawl.

So I gave up on the idea and never thought much about ham again till I was approaching my O levels and was forced to study *The History of Mr Polly* by H.G. Wells. As with most books that one is *forced* to read, I have few memories of Wells' story of the adventures of the little northern draper, but one line has always stuck in my mind — "married with ham, buried with ham." Very true, I thought. In that claustrophobic little part of south Yorkshire in which I was reared, not unlike the society in which Mr. Polly was trapped, the offering of ham to a guest was among the greatest compliments that one could bestow. Not that it was always served with good grace. Whenever "company" was expected, the first thing was always to get in a "slice o' 'am." It was expensive stuff- and probably quite ordinary although I was never allowed a taste – but the purchase and offering of it was a mark of welcome, even if on occasions the welcome was less than whole-hearted. I say that because I recall the visit of a distant relative marked by an acrimonious dispute as to whether she was worthy of having "a bit of 'am got in" because it was well remembered that she had not paid us a similar compliment on one of our rare visits to her. However, the ham was duly bought and offered, but the entire ritual was underscored with the thought that she was no better than she should have been, not hamworthy. But then ham hardly entered my life after that.

Until 35 years after my bitter disappointment on the road to Bridlington, I started to keep pigs of my own. I suppose I had forgotten what ham should be like, having been ground down over the years by the subtle degradations in this matchless food engineered by the mass-producers, food technologists and marketing teams. But when we had killed one of our first pigs, sent it to the butcher for a raditional curing and brought it home and boiled it, such was the exquisite flavour, scent and texture that I quickly realised that we have been robbed. With our implicit consent, someone, somewhere has dragged a glorious meat from our plates and left in its place a commodity that is a sham – definitely not a ham.

That moment was a turning point. I knew from then onwards that it was my duty to unearth the secrets of ham-making that had been buried under half a century of commercialisation of the product and exploitation of the pig. This book is the story of a journey which took me to stinking corners of many farms where pigs are kept; to butchers' back rooms where hams are cured and sausages formed; the black world of the slaughterer and the fondly remembered stys of the cottagers' pigs.

But the journey took me in an equally important direction too; for I was soon to learn that getting a good ham from a lousy pig is as impossible as making a silk purse out of a sow's ear. For every humiliation that the noble ham, bacon, pork pie or sausage has suffered over the last thirty years since the production of food became an industrial process, the pig has suffered far worse. The pig sty is obsolete, replaced by intensive units which turn out fat pigs more cheaply and rapidly than any farmer a mere fifty years ago could have imagined. The sows are confined, screened from the daylight, never allowed to employ their highly sensitive noses rooting joyously for grubs. It is no way to treat an intelligent animal like a pig, and so my journey took me not merely along the food-strewn path, littered with the luscious and varied foods the pig can give us, but also in search of a better and more humane way to rear pigs, which affords them the respect they deserve and have earned over centuries of faithful service.

As far as the food was concerned, I was searching for the real thing; the ham that I always imagined would be on those plates in that wooden hut that stood by the road; food so glorious and special that the secrets of making it were known to only a few. If only I could find these magicians and unlock their secrets then their skills would become mine and I would have to pine no longer for my ham feast. Of course, many will argue that ham then was no better than it is now, it is just that we are into an age of deep nostalgia where nothing is as good as it was. Well, there is indeed evidence to suggest that ham has never ever been as good as it was. It is possible that it is one of those foods where the anticipation of it is always greater than the eventual feast — a bit like Christmas. The great chef, Alexis Soyer, an Albert Roux of his time who left Paris in 1830 and became chef at the Reform Club and wrote many best-selling cookery books, tells the tale in his *A Shilling Cookery for The People of 1854*, of a disappointing journey to Devon.

> . . . About six months ago I was on a visit to our excellent friend, William Tucker, Esq., of Coriton Park, near Axminster, Devon, when all the neighbourhood was searched to get a couple of home-cured country hams; however, no such thing was to be found; everyone of them bought were dried to chips. The fat of the first we operated on, when sawn in two, (for we could not cut it in the ordinary way), was of a blackish yellow, and the meat of the same colour as rotten wood, only much harder. Being anxious to see the person who had so effectively "preserved" this ham, a very natty, clean old woman was brought to me; and on showing her the bone, and asking her for the receipt (recipe) she said she did not know how it was done, but her son Thomas did, and she knew he would be glad to give me the receipt, to which proposition I strongly objected.

I have included some recipes (excluding that of her son Thomas) and I hope that you will find, on whichever road you travel, a perfect ham. There are fewer finer feasts to be had from the whole of a hog.

Part One

1

I knew that at some stage in my travels I would have to confront the dismal process of the making mass-produced hams; those slivers of salty slime that are packed between plastic and chemically preserved to a point where their shelf-life is as long as vintage wine. Alas, unlike wine, they do not improve with age. You can understand, I hope, why I might want to put off as long as possible that day I had to turn up at some factory and don silly rubber boots and crisp white trilby hat. No one who cured the sort of ham I am looking for ever wore a hair-net. So, like a child picking at the cherries and leaving the tasteless sponge at the bottom of the trifle, I set off on a short tour of the north of England, where I was born and bred, and which I guessed from hazy memory might bring me closest to my goal. What that might be, I could not be certain till I had arrived but, like love, one knows when one is smitten and I felt sure I would be in no doubt when the moment came that I confronted the ultimate ham.

Why go north? Is not Wiltshire as famous for its hams as York? Bath has its pork chaps, Barnsley only its chop. If I am honest, I chose to go north more or less for a change of landscape; the ripples of eastern England which I view and till on a daily basis have their charm, but they are as a mere tinkling of the ivories compared with the symphonic splendours of the Pennines, Lakes and Fells. Anyway, it is possible that it takes a meaty landscape to instil a meaty frame of mind. Suffolk, famed as the bread-basket of England for its climate and soil, perfectly suited to the growing of bread-making wheat, has a truly floury landscape. It looks as though it had been sifted, the lumps removed, and only the merest undulations remaining where the hand of the Maker holding his sieve has twitched. By contrast, hard crags make for hard men, and industry makes for hard work. It is not to diminish the daily toil of the farm worker in any way to say that the industries of the North, driven by steam, steel, cotton and coal, could not be tackled on an empty belly. What better and cheaper way to fill it than with all that

13

the pig can provide? Anyway; it is the only reason I can come up with for the Pork Shop being a predominantly northern phenomenon. It is true that Pork Butchers have escaped to the south, but they have not travelled well. I felt certain that true pork, ham and bacon was only to be found in true pork shops, and to find them I would have to head north.

I had fixed myself a pleasant little circuit of Yorkshire and Cumbria, planning to leave the farm on a Monday morning in early December and be back by Friday. Four days are about as long as the stock will allow a leave of absence: cattle knock down fences, sheep dive through hedges, pigs burrow beneath electric barriers. Yes, four days was safe. I dare take no longer. I was packing on the Sunday evening for an early departure the next morning when the phone rang. It was a butcher.

Here I must confess to a shameful manipulation. I have been writing my weekly column in *The Times* sufficiently long for me to have a direct line of communication with those who read it. In the past I have asked them for the recipe for the pudding made famous by Hardy called frumenty, and collected at least a hundred letters on that one. I caused national debate on the killing of rats and the grinding of oats into porridge. Now, I had decided to set a ball rolling which was marked "ham". I cannot remember precisely the way I phrased it but my piece had a desperate tone about it; it was the pleading of a man who thought that good bacon was a thing of the past, and what was he to do about it? I awaited the mail bag.

"You don't know me," the butcher began, "but I was reading your piece today." He paused, and then hardly able to contain himself, announced, "I've got some black 'uns comin' out tomorrow. I could get 'em out right now if you want to see 'em." Hang on, I thought. It was eleven o'clock at night. Knowing he was local from something he had said, I agreed to see him on my way north. His "black 'uns" were, of course, sides of Suffolk sweet-cure bacon. It is a cure which darkens the skin by immersion in black treacle and ale, and an oak-smoking gives them the final ebony touch. A promising start.

I went to Debenham, as near a picture of a perfect Suffolk village as one could wish for: pink, yellow and white cottages line either side of the main street separated from the road by wide grassy verges. I used to come here to Aldous the harness-maker but after he retired and his apprentice moved to premises of his own, the shop which had known only the smell of leather for two centuries, where the floors had been worn into potholes by the twitching feet of the saddler as he sat at his

14

bench, where the relentless cut of the knife and stab of the needle had worn smooth holes in the benches, was gutted and taken over by ranks of videos. The business did not last; a couple of centuries of testimony to the skills of the men who had worked in that shop had been needlessly junked.

F.E. Neave, Curers of Bacons and Hams, is one of those shops which could easily have gone the way of the harness-maker's. But it was saved by David Allen, and born again. Allen was forced out of the local market town where one way traffic systems around his butchery and next-door bakery gave him claustrophobia, he was quick to spot that Neave's was an establishment worth keeping, and he was not going to let it disappear.

I ducked between newly plastered beams, props supporting ceilings that had been lifted or dropped, concrete floors that seemed only just to have dried. Even the sign above the shop with its gilt swirls and lettering was new. All that remained of the old tradition was the spirit which Allen had tried to capture.

A heavy metal door was pulled aside as if one was about to meet a prisoner on death row. David Allen stood in his cell, hands gloved in rubber, turning sides of bacon and ham in a vat of brown, sweet-smelling brine.

"Hell!" he cried, "people come in here and ask if I'm running a four-ale bar. I prefer it nearer the smoker." He pulled his chilled hands out of a tub of brine, hams lurking just beneath the surface, like sharks. "Warmer. I like to be warmer as I get older. I tell you, when you've had your hands in the fridge for three hours, it can give you some stick."

Behind him hung sides of bacon, dark brown and drying after immersion in the cure. What exactly the cure might be was one of those questions to which I never expected an answer. In principle, all curing appears to be the same: there is salt which is the preservative, sometimes saltpetre which merely acts to keep the ham pink and not grey, and flavourings; it is as simple as that; which amounts to saying there is nothing to Coca Cola except sugar, brown colourings and something to give it a kick. Come to think of it, Allen's cure did look more like Coca Cola than anything else, except his was more concentrated and not at all fizzy. I asked for the recipe and to my great surprise got an answer. "There's 32 pound of treacle, 40 pound of black sugar – that's Foot Sugar from Mauritius. No water at all. I just top it up with beer from the Queen Vic." He pointed to a freshly delivered barrel in the corner. The Queen Vic is a renowned public house

15

in the nearby village of Earl Soham famed for its home-brewed ales. So, we have ale, sugar, treacle and that's it? "Oh no," says Allen, "then there's my secret cures." He was not going to go any further but by repeating the list, "that's the salt, saltpetre and . . ." I hoped he might fall into my trap and finish the sentence. . . . "and my secret bits and bobs." Damn him.

We went on a whirlwind tour of the hinterland. "I don't serve in the shop. People don't want to see me. This is what I call the Debenham cure", his commentary matches that of the race commentator . . . "it's a lighter cure. We do minimum injection of our hams. We aren't in the business of selling water."

I had decided before I set out on this odyssey that the true test of a butcher would be where he stood on fat. As a breeder of fat pigs myself (those who eat them say they cannot remember tasting anything better) I am convinced that flavour comes from fat. I have never suggested you have to eat the fat. If you do not want to, you can edge it to the side of your plate. I decided I would question all my butchers on their view of fat and listen carefully to their replies. If I heard treacherous words along the lines of ". . . we have to respond to the market . . . we have to think about our health don't we" . . . or, worst of all . . . "we must compete with those supermarket chaps, after all, they know what they are doing, don't they?" I would mark a man down severely.

"Well, "said Allen," I like a hog pig, or a gilt with half an inch of fat. No more. Some like an inch, some no fat at all. But I have converted people to fat on pork. I really have." He scored well so far.

We went into the house, once more past the hams bobbing like miniature whales in the sweet alcoholic brown sea. Allen took out some photographs he had taken during the renovation. "Look at that, it was terrible. When we first came, they were still cutting up meat in the open air." I thought it looked rather honest. "These rusty old bins were the curing vats. Terrible." I nodded, but I was not sure. I doubt anyone has had a moment's illness from a ham cured in one of Neave's old bins and, like the teapot that is never washed out for fear of losing its magic properties, I wondered; could it just be that when they threw out the rusty old bins, they were throwing out the baby with the brine? "He's still around, old Mr Neave. He'll tell you a thing or two," offered Allen. I took careful note.

Intoxicated by the smell of ale, salt and smoke, and with every taste-bud in my mouth pleading for a bacon sandwich, I walked out of the shop into the freezing blast of an easterly wind which cuts through the

Suffolk villages like Allen's cleaver through a joint. Frozen already by slow ambles through refrigerator after refrigerator, I got in the car, turned the heat to full, and set off for the north.

Are you fully aware of how difficult it is to buy a bacon sandwich anywhere between East Anglia and the West Riding of Yorkshire? You can discount roadside cafes of the Little Chef and Happy Eater type, for there is not sufficient within a simple bacon sandwich for them to take hold of, twist, target, value-add, and then sell to us at a high price. So it has to be "bacon-burgers" or the "great farmhouse breakfast". These will not satisfy the needs of a man who requires two or three slices of crisply fried bacon (not too lean) between two slices of white processed bread (no wholemeal; no goodness allowed) which have been spread with butter which melts on contact with the hot bacon and spreads the blend of butter and bacon fat through the two slices of blotter. It is essential to the full enjoyment of the bacon sandwich that grease should dribble down one's chin. I have tried bacon sandwiches made with brown bread, but they do not work.

My only hope was to find a cafe in a lay-by. These need no Tourist Board rosettes or Michelin stars; you count their success by the number of lorries parked on either side. Appearances can be deceptive. I have eaten gloriously in filthy hovels where junior health inspectors are sent to have their stomachs and their sensitivities hardened; whereas glossy trailers with gas, plumbing and running water have often served indifferent fare.

Alas, one also needs a certain amount of courage before entering these pull-ins, and a certain sensitivity to the unique atmosphere. There is an old Leyland coach which parks not far from where we live which looks as though it may have seen service in the closing days of World War 2. I suspect it is immobile, for it sprouts a chimney and awnings which would not travel very far if the monstrosity exceeded five miles an hour. One day, I bravely decided to pay a call. I went in, to be hit by the temperature which was at Turkish bath levels, then by the pungency of the air which was fetid with cooking fat (lard, not sunflower), cigarette smoke and the bodily odours of a dozen hairy men. I was sensitive enough not to ask to see the menu, nor to ask for coffee. A man with an aluminium catering teapot aggressively inquired, "Sugar?" There was no question of my having anything other than his tea, and there was an implicit threat that turning down his sugar might well have all twelve lorry drivers on their feet giving me a good thumping. It is not a place to sit and read the *Guardian* over a cappuccino.

Few of these ad-hoc roadside cafes offer anything to suggest there might be a warm welcome inside. There are huge padlocks hanging from massive rusty hasps on the doors; the windows are covered with steel mesh, broken glass patched with sodden and crumbling hardboard. They are real places to a have shoot-out. The Happy Eaters and Little Chefs on the other hand are all welcome but little else. Food may be wholesome but is standardised. The youthful staff who accost you as you enter and enquire "smokin' or non smokin" ' and try to look as though they cared, are merely in training for the day when they will have their own Leyland bus in a lay-by and can squint at you like witches — "sugar, boiled frogs, sheep' eyeballs?' So, lacking the courage to face anything the A1 had to offer, I sped past Diane's Diner and Moll's Pull In and arrived at a petrol station which offered amongst its microwaveable rolls, a bacon and cheese. I blasted it into life for the required thirty seconds, took a cup of reconstituted tea from the machine and thought this a poor start to a committed ham-hunter's tour of the north of England.

With time in hand, I dived off in the direction of Sheffield, my home town. The "pork shop", as the pork-only butchers of the north were called, was as much a feature of my childhood as anything I can remember. There were many of them, each with a jealously guarded reputation, each with a loyal band of customers. Anyone deciding to change their allegiance gave no less thought to it than to swapping political parties. What sticks in my mind was not the meat, but the sheer beauty of the shops and the appetising smells that drifted onto an otherwise grim pavement. I remembered one in particular, and set off to see if it was still there.

It was called *Kelseys*, of Wadsley Bridge, and stood on the corner of a row of shops facing a school where my grandad was school crossing warden. He was a carpenter, a man of some talent who made the revolving doors for Sheffield's Locarno ballroom. In his retirement, he had taken on the job of taking children across the road carrying not the lollipop (which I remember being introduced) but a substantial oblong board which carried "HALT" and a torch of safety, now hijacked by the Tory party as their emblem. Grandad would never have carried that torch if he'd known the Conservatives were going to call it theirs. He was always a Labour man. And a good pork shop man.

To fill the time between his morning and teatime duties, he fixed himself up a work-bench in the school's basement boiler-room and practised his fading craft. He would call in at Kelseys, the pork butcher, on his way to work to buy his pork sandwich for dinner.

Kelseys had their name in large gold letters above the shop door, the window full of equally golden, bread-crumbed joints of bacon, gammons and ham. The sandwiches were no mere trifles; a large, white cake almost as big as a dinner plate was sliced open and liberally spread with pork dripping of Kelsey's own making - the sort with the gravy at the bottom of the tub. The pork, still warm from the oven, was sliced in front of you and lavish helpings were heaped upon the bread. Then a chunky slice of sage and onion stuffing and the lid was closed. "I'll 'av a bit 'o cracklin," Grandad would remind them. "Oh, sorry Sam," they would say, and open the sandwich and slip a chunk in. We would take this over the road and down into the basement where the boiler rumbled. The air was filled with acrid smoke from the coke but made pleasant by the sweet smell of the pot of carpenter's wood- glue bubbling in the corner and the fresh scent of wood shavings. Here we would spend days; me learning how to hold a chisel or drive a nail, he eating his pork sandwich. Bless him. When he finally retired, he had only his pension to live on and I doubt he ever afforded a pork sandwich again.

It goes without saying that on my return trip 35 years later, I found Kelseys to have long since disappeared under a road-widening scheme. But Fairest the Funeral Director, a name I remembered, had the good sense to build his parlour well back from the road and his premises remained intact. It was typical of Wadsley Bridge; they were always giving more thought to death than they ever did to the good things in life, and they now have what they deserve; a first class burial service and nowhere to buy a pork sandwich. Even the old Dewhursts to which you went, even in those days, when you were hard up and couldn't afford any better, had been taken over by a building society. The whole of Wadsley Bridge which I remembered as a poor but proud little corner of Sheffield had turned into a tip. They had carried out improvements here, built supermarkets there, but none of it seemed to be to any organised plan which might have been to improve the area. But the whole of Sheffield seemed like that. There was still a steel industry when I was a kid; the sky was alight at night with the glare of the furnaces in Attercliffe, Tinsley and Rotherham. The only claim the Sheffield steel industry has to fame now is as the builder of the Iraqi super-gun. The council has erected a limp little sign at the city boundary which reads "If it doesn't say Sheffield, It isn't Made in Sheffield" as if anyone still went looking for the word "Sheffield" stamped on anything.

I drove into Hillsborough, famous for its football tragedy. But as I parked the car, the first shop I saw set my heart pounding and my taste buds on edge. *F. Funk. Est 1892. Champion Yorkshire Sausage Maker.* I pressed my face to the window and was well rewarded with pressed face looking back at me. Honest. Pressed Face – £1.65 a quarter. This was clearly a pork shop that was not afraid to address the issues. I have heard of this delicacy – pressed face – being called pork cheese, bacon bits or any other cover-up name; but there is no avoiding the fact that what is on offer is bits of pigs' faces, cooked and pressed. It is pressed face. The rest of the window did not disappoint: black puddings, boiled shoulder (again, no marketing euphemism). There were oat-cakes too; flat, circular, floppy cakes, totally unlike the biscuity Scottish oatcake, leavened with a little baking powder I remember them being slipped into the frying pan after the egg ,to mop up the bacon fat as they gently fried till slightly crisp.

"Hello luv, what der yer wan' luv?" Oatcakes please, and a sausage roll.

Just as I was looking at a tray labelled "Chinese stir-fry pork" and thinking that I could hardly blame them for moving with the times, I spotted floury white bread-cakes exactly like the ones I had seen in Kelseys thirty-five years before. Then my eye was quickly taken to a huge vat of pork dripping with a massive spatula stuck in it, ready to smear one of those cakes with its lardy goodness. It was mid-after-noon, and alas my appetite was well and truly dulled by the microwaved bacon sandwich, so I only gazed at that lard like a lad eye-ing his first girl and not sure he is up to it. I was entranced. The girl had to ask me twice "One sausage roll or two, luv?" Just the one.

I went to the cafe next door for a cup a tea. " Eh, its that cow'd (cold) I wish as I had a drop o' whisky ter pur in it f' yer." It was indeed bit-terly cold. "Bu' its too cowd t' snow" insisted the woman in the teashop. I walked back to the car and once again paused for a moment outside F. Funk. Est 1892. I noticed he was close to the Simpkins Medicated Sweets factory where my mother had worked when I was very young. She graduated from there to the Bassetts Liquorice Allsort Factory from where she regularly brought home the mis-shapes. My health went steadily downhill after that, deprived as it was of Simpkins invigorating influence.

I got back into the car, heating turned up full once again against the cold wind, and carefully unwrapped the bag which contained the sausage roll. I bit into it. The pastry was crumbly, the meat filling firm, solid and tasty. It might have been home-made; it was certainly made by hand and not extruded by machinery. It sat nicely in my tummy as the dusk fell and I headed north along the spine of the Pennines. By the time I was going over the moor that drops down into Halifax, I regretted having eaten that sausage roll. The temperature took a dive as I climbed at least a thousand feet along a winding road over a spot so bleak that it made Wuthering Heights look like a Holiday Inn. It started to rain, and blow a gale, and I felt the car behave in an odd way and put it down to cross-winds. As I reached the summit I saw stop-lights ahead of me, and braked. Nothing happened. Black ice. With the greatest of luck I came to a halt 30 yards behind the car in front just as the flashing blue lights of a police-car were heading towards us. "The grit lorry's cumin' " said the officer, and forbade us to go any fur-ther. I got out of the car and tried to walk round to the boot, but the road was like a rink and I clung to the side of the car like a beginner on skates. I checked the sausage-roll bag. Perhaps my memory deceived me and I had bought two. No, there was nothing there. A sec-ond sausage-roll would have been very welcome atop this bleak spot. I slithered back from the boot to the driver's door and found the ice was already building on the windows where the driven rain was freezing solid. With some difficulty I pulled the door open. The grit lorry was half an hour coming; long enough to impress upon me that one should never travel these wild places in winter without an emergency sausage roll. If, for some reason, the grit lorry did not show up, we could always have crumbled some of the pastry on the road, and got traction that way.

I spent the next morning in the town of Settle, high on the Yorkshire Dales and glad to put the grim West Riding behind me. I had spent too many years surrounded by sandstone walling blackened by soot to take any pleasure in what, to an eye that has not seen it before, may well be interesting vernacular architecture. But to me it was just a mucky mess of black houses made hideous by added plastic window frames and mock-Georgian front doors. Not only is the architecture a jumble, this entire corner of Yorkshire is a tangle of Huddersfields, Keigthleys, Halifaxs and Bradfords. As you follow the road signs each town blurs into the next and the sooted stone walls and houses just go on and on. But Settle is in real countryside, and has the feel of an alive market town. It has shrugged off its relatives in the industrial parts of Yorkshire in a way that its more famous neighbour, Skipton, does not seem to have quite managed. The West Riding has Skipton within its reach and seems to beckon the town with its finger as if to say, "you are one of us, you know. Don't put on airs."

It was market day in Settle. Stallholders flogged the usual tat that can only be found on sale in any British market. There were boot-leg tapes and videos, imitation brand-name jeans that would shrink to fluff the instant they hit the tumble drier; there were dried lumps of cheese being offered by a man in a grubby apron, and a threatening drip on the end of his nose. A chap took a large ladies' nightdress off its plastic coat-hanger, stirred his tea with the end of it and quietly slipped the nightdress back on it. I headed for the newsagent and as I was coming out with my newspaper, a five-year old girl was being sick in the doorway. A large, shambling figure - probably her grandmother – was standing next to her as the customers emerging with their copies of the *Dalesman, Womans Weekly* or *Telegraph.* "Shi's just showin' off, aren't yer luv?" she said in a stage whisper. If this was showing off, I didn't want to be around for her next trick. Come to think of it, I remember from my own childhood how all ills were in some way your fault, and symptoms were only displayed with the intent of embarrassing parents. I remember too being scolded for limping in shoes two sizes too small with the words, "pick yer feet up, walk proper, and stop showin' me up!" Living down there among adult legs, ankles had always held a certain fear for me too. I have vivid memories of menopausal northern ladies spending as much time putting bandages on their ankles as most normal women spend applying make-up to their faces. Thick, crepe bandages. As I strolled down a back street of Settle now, a figure hobbled towards me, heavily clad, heavily bandaged around both limbs. "How are they luv?" asked a passer by. "They'll never be any better. Nay. They'll never be any better now." And she hobbled on her way, resigned to her orthopaedic fate and enjoying every minute of it. Resignation runs strongly in the blood of anyone born north of Nottingham. They feel that fate has a greater hold on them than on other mortals and rejoice perversely in bowing to its will. An X-ray and visit to a good doctor would do that old girl no harm, but no, "they'll never be any better."

On the way back to the car I passed a bakery and spotted a treat I had not seen for many year; a Yorkshire Curd tart. This is a true delicacy made from curds (as in curds and whey) sweetened and fortified with raisins and baked in a crust. If there was one thing that could deflect me from my search for hams, it was a slice of Yorkshire curd tart. Then I suddenly thought of the little girl, "showin' off" in the newsagent's doorway, and decided it was time to put Yorkshire behind me.

I was heading for Cumbria, but precisely where I was not certain. I was looking for the village of Waberthwaite, but none of my maps showed it. Several months previously, I had been in the market town of Ulverston and it was there that I spotted a slice of ham in a shop window. It was so pink, perfect and delicious-looking that I asked the shopkeeper where it had come from. Having got the address, in Waberthwaite, I vowed to pay a visit.

In retrospect, the shopkeeper may have been misleading me a little for I got the certain impression that Waberthwaite and Ulverston were quite close, sort of round the next corner. But Ulverston is one of those confusing places which feels untouched and remote despite being well-placed on the tourist trail of the southern Lakes. It remains a frontier-town. It would not be difficult to imagine a wild-west shoot out in the high street. I spent the whole day humming " Ulverston, oh Ulverston" to the tune of *Galveston*, and expected any minute that the sheriff would ride into town. Even the grocer's shop in which I had spotted the ham was 50 years behind the times with huge tins of tea on painted wooden shelves, bacon being cut on a hand-wound slicing machine, wooden floor-boards and piles of locally baked bread.

Under the impression, then, that Waberthwaite was no more than an hour and a half from Settle, I dawdled. I stopped by an enticing sign announcing "local Cumbrian produce" and popped into a tiny but perfectly (too perfectly) fitted-out shop: pine shelves, slate floors, diffused lighting, the works. Here were jams with Cumbrian labels, and smoked sausages too, and packets of proudly labelled "Dry Cured Cumbrian Bacon." I seized on a packet and asked if it was cured locally and by whom, sensing a lead which might set me off in a new direction. "Oh, we buy all over the place. Some of it comes from Scotland, Yorkshire, all over." It was about as Cumbrian as a Glaswegian on a day trip to Windermere. Nor do I see how you can honestly sell Cumbrian Strawberry Jam when any fool knows that strawberries will not grow in any quantity in that wild part of the world. Alas, I had paid for my bacon and didn't want to spoil a nice day with a row.

I decided to press on to Waberthwaite, and Richard Woodall whose hams and sausages bear the Royal Warrant. He had given me directions on the phone but I had paid little attention for I knew that once there he could not be too difficult to find. The only clue that stuck in my mind was that he had told me to look out for a pub called the Brown Cow. I drove on, getting more nervous, and decided to stop and ask the way.

I was in the town of Broughton-in-Furness; another tight huddle of dwellings with their backs to the fierce westerly weather and a less than inviting prospect of more grey houses and damp-looking people. I dropped into the butcher's who were sure to know where Cumbria's most famous curer of hams was to be found. She did. "Do you want to go over the top?" she asked. "I just want to get there," was my reply. "Follow the main road till the Brown Cow, and take the left fork. You'll see the Post Office." The Brown Cow! I must find the Brown Cow. She assured me it was only half an hour away and so with a little time to spare, I decided on a bite of lunch.

"The Rule of the Road. Teas with Hovis" said the peeling sign that swung in the increasing wind. This was Haskets tea shop. It had a wide selection of three buns in the window and, worryingly for just after 1.00 pm, no diners at all. I went in and sat down at one of the plastic veneered tables and looked around at the tea/bakery/sweet-shop/grocery. It had bits of everything, and nothing of anything at all. You could not shop comprehensively here if you wanted, and it is hard to envisage why you should come out of your way for a packet of tea if they did not also stock the sugar. "I'm off to Waberthwaite," I said, asking for tea. "Are you going over the top?" was the reply. "I just want to get there, I don't care which way I go. Ham sandwich please." "No ham. Turkey?" Amazing isn't it. Here was this shop, less than ten miles from potentially some of the finest hams in the country, and she did not have any ham. I suppose it would be too Cumbrian, too local. If it had come down from Glasgow she might be keener to sell it – it would still be Cumbrian, of course. I settled for a miserable turkey roll and a lady scurried away taking an inordinate length of time to place a slice of bird between two buttered halves of bread. The remaining lady immediately engaged in a close-headed conversation with a shopper in muted tones designed to avoid me over-hearing. I caught a few "she dids" and "she didn'ts" It was clearly some kind of moral shoot-out and so I hid behind the newspaper in case the scandal being discussed was too strong for my tender ears.

24

I have never been so happy in my life to see a brown cow, or should I say the Brown Cow. Waberthwaite was nowhere near where I had imagined it to be. Rather than nestling in a Wordsworthian cleft in a fell, it lay almost on the coast in the far west of Cumbria at the foot of the fells, but with its toes more firmly planted in the Irish Sea than on the hills. I bore left as directed and soon found the tidiest and smartest village post office in the realm. It had spotless written all over it. It was marked with a white signboard, lettered in gold and bearing the royal crest – Richard Woodall. I drove past looking for a parking space, and having a little time to spare I was lured towards the coast by a sign that said "Road Liable to Flooding" I drove as far as I dared, not knowing the state of the tide and whether it would cut me off, then I turned and stopped and looked. Woodall had got himself a prime site; high misty fells capped with snow were his backdrop and a marshy estuary was the stage on which he played out his dramatic curing of hams.

I entered the shop and found myself in a world where Emmerdale Farm meets Fortnum and Mason. The newly-built shelves of solid, quality, hardwood were stacked (not littered as in your average rural shop) with all the usual necessities of village life; custard powder, washing-up liquid, and jellies. Next to the wooden counter was the post office itself which looked to be no more than a desk in the corner; the sort of desk at which a teacher might have sat at the Victorian village school. Walking from the post office desk towards the back of the shop, all sense of place is suspended. You are certainly no longer in a mere village store. Hams hang from hooks on the ceiling, chill counters display perfectly sliced bacon and sausages. Slices of ham are sealed in gilded packets. The staff wore maroon jackets, as if they were working at the Ritz or Savoy; one carved at a hunk of gammon as if he were performing the most delicate of surgical operations. Noisy Americans came into the shop as if they owned the place. "I'll certainly have a slice of that," said the loudly-dressed one. "I'm sorry,' said the maroon-coated chap with the carving knife, "these is orders," and he scraped gently at the slice he had just cut to remove any smears that might spoil the perfection of it. He slipped it carefully into a packet and then, reluctantly in my estimation, gave the American his full attention. I stood quietly, waiting for Richard Woodall, as nervous as if I were meeting a king.

I need not have worried. This fine-featured man welcomed me warmly and we went to his cosy but plain sitting room which was part of the post office building but very much the other side of the door. He laid on tea, and tea-cakes, and the story of Woodall's ham unfolded.

"It was all started by Hannah and Richard Woodall, early last century, who had five girls and a son. Alas, Richard died on his way home from church and Hannah, looking for some way of keeping the family together, decided to open a grocer's shop. The son, who was called Jackson, helped his mother. He would go out and slaughter pigs and bring them back to cure. And they did well. I've got a prize ticket from the International Dairy Show held at Kilburn in 1879. It says First Prize for 6 British Hams. They became very well known. MPs bought 'em. By 1900 it was a countrywide operation, but the fact is it was still an out of the way place. It's still a bit of a fag to get here.

"We've always had pigs here. Cumberland pigs. They were a shorter, rougher version of a Large White. Flop ears, bit like a Welsh. Good scavenging pigs they were; a cheap sort of pig and they made quite a large carcass. Remember, they killed them when they were two and a half years old, Now we kill 'em at six months."

The developments in pig-rearing that have taken place since the demise of the Cumberland pig have been astonishing, and neither in the best interests of the pig or the consumer. As Woodall remembers, in 1953 a food conversion ratio of a pig was four to one; i.e. four pounds of food to put one pound of weight on an animal. Now the feeding is scientifically forced to demand a ratio of two to one. Something has to pay for that urgency and the first victim is flavour. "The Meat and Livestock Commission have a lot to answer for," says Woodall. "And the feed makers who are preoccupied with putting on meat and not fat. The modern generation of eaters do not realise that meat is supposed to have flavour – for God's sake!" I was warming to Woodall. "The trouble is, most of them cannot remember what the real stuff tasted like. I sold a ham to a lady a few years back and she rang up to say it was off. I went round there straight away thinking that perhaps she had not cooked it properly, but it looked fine. I asked for a knife and took a slice. It tasted gorgeous. I gave her her money back, took the ham home and we had it that Christmas and it was one of the best we have ever had. There is a blandness today and it all boils down to economics. They inject it, tumble it, mess it around. Pork will accept 75% of its own weight of moisture and so they simply pump water into it."

He leaned forward in his chair, "I don't! The way I cure hams, I am taking water out of them all the time and that is why the flavour gets better and better." By now I was drooling, my nose picking up the scents drifting in from the shop. When he invited me through to see how his curing works, I did not hesitate.

It was like a winter scene from a Disney movie. Hams are piled three feet high, sitting on a huge slab in a chilly room , dressed in salt and looking as if there has been a fresh fall of snow. And that is all that happens to them; they sit there for a month undisturbed by any injecting, tumbling or man-handling.

"We rub them well with a mixture of salt and saltpetre," says Woodall, "the saltpetre it just for colouring, to keep the ham pink. Then we put them on a bed of salt an inch and a half thick. We use dairy salt. It cures in a month, just lying there. Of course, there's an art in making sure they are not too salty or too dry. When they're cured, we wash off the salt and they hang to dry for three days or so. There is no shortcut in this business. You cannot rush a ham. If you want your money back quickly you ought to forget this business. Some of these hams can hang for year. That's your money up on the hook."

From the peaceful chill room with its hams lying sedately in a sublime permafrost, drying, salting and increasing in flavour as they sat, we moved to another room where hams that had already been cured were hung to dry in a gentle draught. There were hundreds of them, hanging like huge bats; some covered with a layer of thick mould that would send the squeamish scampering ("We had it tested. It's harmless. We just wash it off"). All looked rich and full of concentrated flavour; the moisture had slowly evaporated making the taste more intense as the days ticked by. We closed the door and let them slumber, and moved outside.

Woodall is no butcher, he is a grocer. He is no farmer either although the pigs from which he produces his hams live no more than a hundred yards from where the hind quarters of their sisters, brothers, sons and daughters, deliciously hang. We slid back the door of the long, low asbestos shed and although this may at first sight appear to be the unpleasant face of intensive pig farming, on close questioning it is clear that the ham is no more highly regarded than the pig from which it comes; both are treated like royalty. "We have 180 sows and its been a closed herd since 1976. We haven't bought in a pig since then – reared our own. We use no growth promoters, no hormones, no antibiotics. Expert opinion said it couldn't be done," said Woodall proudly, "but we have done it. You've got to give pigs a chance. They're lovely clean animals." One begins to wonder about the value of expert opinion and admire the bravery of those who set themselves against the trend of modern opinions, but Woodall and his family have been at the game too long to rely on anything but their instincts when it comes to ham and pigs. As we strolled back to the shop I spotted a girl deftly knotting huge lengths of Cumberland sausage. "These are for the Royal Yacht Britannia," Woodall told me, "we have a warrant as suppliers of Cumberland sausages to the Queen, but actually I think it's Philip that scoffs most of 'em."

I drove from Cumbria, clutching a pound of royal sausages, with the intention of heading home. Instead, I paused for the night in the Yorkshire Dales at an ancient inn bequeathed to the National Trust on the condition that it should never serve drink. Its present tenants, recognising this a something of a threat to their hotel trade, relax the rule and allow you to bring your own bottle. They had warned me in advance. On my way back through Broughton-in-Furness, opposite the tea-room where I had taken lunch, the local grocer had a few bottles of distinctly acidic-looking red wine. Bravely I choose something Romanian. A couple of hours later I was back in Yorkshire and snug in a room in the tiny hotel at the foot of a massive hill. The landlord went on a bit too long about his "gut-rot" and how he must avoid drink so I was left with the entire bottle of Romanian wine to myself. It was vile. It could have stripped hairs off a pig's back or dissolved boars' teeth. I was served delicious roast pork (by coincidence for they did not know why I was in the area) with perfect crackling followed by a warming winter steamed pudding. All this reacted violently with the poisonous red wine and I spent the night with the most violent stomach cramps I have ever experienced.

I dreaded breakfast for I had offered the hotelier the royal Cumberland sausages to cook and she in return had boasted of the ones her own butcher produced. Accordingly she offered to cook both for my breakfast by way of a test. I politely cleared my plate, but it was painful and my innards were in far too much turmoil to assess anything. By a whisker, Woodall's seemed better, but after Romanian red wine I would not guarantee any value-judgements made about food. We shall just have to assume Prince Philip knows best, as I am sure he would wish us to do.

Aching too much even to contemplate lunch, I drove on and stopped in Masham. It was market day and the sleety rain was bucketing down on similar dreary stalls to the ones I had seen in Settle a few days before. I made for a cafe on the corner where a woman was serving to a man standing outside, an individual Christmas pudding laden with a bright yellow custard which was clearly a product of a chemist and not a cook. It did not bother the customer who was being served through an open window. The rain dripped from the gutter into his pudding, making plopping sounds as it hit his glutinous custard. "Do yer want any more puddins" he asked. "I've got two sorts. There's deluxe and luxury but all the labels have fallen off and I can't tell which is which." I was standing by the counter now, waiting to order. "What's the difference?" said the woman. "Well," said the man after a spoonful of custard. "one's got brandy in and the other hasn't. Yer can 'av 'em eight for a pound." "Oh, all right then," said the woman, " I'll have a fivers worth and any I don't sell I'll give to me chickens." She slammed the window shut. "Yes?" she said sharply, looking in my direction. I was certainly not going to order a pudding, nor, given the chickens festive and intoxicating diet, anything with eggs.

I dawdled my way home and decided to call in on Ray Buckle who has been chairman of the Pork and Bacon section of the Meat Traders Federation. I expected he would be full of nothing but praise for the virtues of the modern pig and the pork we are served by a majority of his members. I could not have been more wrong. His shop in Robertown is small, undistinguished and in a part of that suburban sprawl which lines the valleys linking Leeds, Huddersfield and all those other places I never managed to untangle. Buckle thinks not a lot of the way the pork business is heading, and coming from a man who must have some influence, this has got to be good news. "People have lost out on flavour," he declares, "they are used to blandness." There is a smell of baking coming from his ovens. "What they do these days is just cover everything with additives. We make polony here. Its just pork, seasoning and binder. We do pork pies up to fourteen pounds in weight – cartwheels we call 'em. We do brawns and haslet like we used to when I was a kid, and we bake our own breadcakes. Nothing is wasted. We always used to use the pork fat for the black puddings but you can't get the blood these days. So we make dripping for chip shops. Good stuff it is – no water in it. Then there's the salt and-pepper pork pies which you don't see anywhere other than round here. The meat in them is grey; they don't want a pink pork pie round here. They're slowly killing everything with additives, killing everything."

This is music to the ears, but it is a tune I had heard before. But the music changed, and he went off onto a different theme. I pricked up my ears. His son Andrew joined in. "They kill pigs too young these days. They're not mature. We don't want lean meat. Since we've been selling pork with more fat on it, sales have increased." He slammed down a pork chop in front of me, and pressed hard on it. "This is what I don't want to see – we call this stuff pissy pork. It smells of piss. The fat doesn't set. It's lousy. It's because they don't castrate pigs any more, and there is no doubt that you can smell 'em. I hate it. I'll happily pay a premium for castrated pig-meat and our supplier knows that's what I want. Either that or a gilt." I left his shop with one of his own sweet mince-pies for company, and a pork pie for later.

What was becoming clear so far, and Buckle had crystallised it in my mind, was that in the good old days pigs lived out of doors with poor diets and grew only slowly. They ended up with a gorgeously mature flavour, but such slow fattening was hardly economic. So pigs were fattened more quickly and that was fine until the fat faddists persuaded us all that fat was bad for us, and attention turned to breeding the fat out of pigs. We ended up with a pig bred to fatten quickly, putting on only meat with little fat. It was good economics but made for poor eating. The flavour, which came from the fat, had been deliberately excluded and even the castration of the boar piglets had been abandoned because it was found that their growing was set back several weeks. So we ended up with lean, tasteless and rank pork; all in the interests of profit. Never has it been more true that when it comes to buying pork or ham, you get what you pay for. Or rather, what the supplier has been willing to pay for.

In order to bring my journey full circle, I decided to return via Debenham and call upon old Mr Neave, the retired butcher who lived across the road from his old shop and who had established the village's reputation for curing hams. He was now 78 and frail, and took a long time coming to the door, but he was still fit enough, so I was told, to stagger across the road into his old shop, and make life a nuisance for them.

"Pigs, sir, are not worth eating these days," he quickly warmed to his theme. "A lovely pig as far as I am concerned," his eyes started to glaze over, "is a castrated pig. You can always tell a boar; it's testicles stick out, you know." He leaned forward to offer me a confidence, "They fornicate with each other as well. Bum-boys I used to call them. You don't want any of them if you want to cure a good ham. That's the trouble with hams these days. I told Mr Gummer (then agriculture minister) all about it. But quite frankly he doesn't know much more than a boy scout, does he? Every farmer round here used to keep a pig or two in a nice strawed sty and they would do their Christmas shopping with the money they got for that pig. I'd go round the farms and kill 'em myself."

Advice for would-be curers came thick and fast. "Never cure a sow, sir, that's 'on hog', as we call it. The smell will be awful when you cut into it. And you must use Barbados sugar. You will also need 28 lb bars of baked salt, which you can't get any more. That's the trouble, sir. You cannot get the ingredients to do a proper, what I would call proper, home-cured ham." He paused only to shout an order for tea to his wife, who never appeared from her little kitchen and merely passed the tea-tray meekly through a half-opened door.

"You've got to make your salt-brine first and do it yourself and then you know it's right. Now, I used to do what I call the fresh egg test. Drop an egg into the water and add salt only till it floats, and no saltier! Mind you, they call it salt but it's not salt." He paused for tea and breath.

"Well, there we are. You now come to the pickle. Well, you can't get the Barbados sugar. It has to run if you hold it in your hand. Then there's black treacle and light treacle and brown sugar and water, and that's your pickle. You can smoke your ham if you like with pure oak sawdust with a bit of applewood, but don't let it get too hot. We used to hang the hams in our cottage to dry and I turned them every three days. Never let a woman touch the brine if it's her time of the month; never let her touch it sir!" The door to the kitchen half opened and we passed back the tea tray with hardly a word.

"Oh, we used to make bootiful hams but it's a lot of work, night and day. And never let the sun shine on your brine, sir. The final step, when your ham has been hanging for about seven or eight months in its bag, is to pack it four inches deep in brewer's grain. But don't let one rest on top of another. You wouldn't want two lying on top of you, would you? Well neither does the ham. The final touch is to give it a bit of a polish, with edible oil. Rub it up sir, till it shine!"

2

Take the road from Cork in south-west Ireland, as my family and I do at least once a year, and head westwards towards the finger of land that holds within its grasp that famous rock called the Fastnet: the last teardrop of Ireland, the final rocky sight that the weeping emigrants saw of their home country when they set sail across the Atlantic to a new life. Stop about five miles short of the coast to savour a small, almost secret kingdom where the people have charm, welcome, honesty and gaiety; and where one or two of them know a thing or two about pigs.

The hundred-mile drive down a brave but crumbling tarmac highway – which boasts of being a Euro-Route but is less well surfaced than most Brussels backyards – prepares you well for your arrival. The names of the towns and villages through which you pass have a gentle rhythm to them, and if you repeat them over and over to yourself as you stare at the signposts (wondering why some distances are in kilometres and others in statute miles) you can slide easily into a trance which will serve you well in the far south-west of Ireland. Those who live there have, of course, become immune to the mantras of the village names and prefer to induce oblivion by consuming rich, black stout. We visitors however need only repeat over and over to ourselves, Clonkilty; Clon . . a . . kil . . ty, Ball-in-spit-tle. Further on we can enjoy Skibbereen and before we reach our destination can roll our tongues relaxedly round Ball-y-de-hob. This is the small town at the head of a very muddy inlet at the head of Roaringwater Bay, and it is in Ballydehob that the annual Slob Races are held. It is some way from being accepted as an Olympic sport and if dope testing were to encompass a chemical search for Guinness residues in the bloodstream of the contestants, none would pass. Slob Racing consists of unassisted and filthy running and stumbling through the waist-high mud at low water. That's it. Then they go to the pub. But at least it has put Ballydehob on the map, sort of. Ballydehob is also the home of the famed "Paddy the Slob from Ballydehob" but all enquiries as to whether he was a character in a song, rude poem or fairy tale have always met with a "sssh" from my wife who has been going to this part of Ireland far longer than I have and is more familiar with the sensitivities of the people. I remember that it was in Ballydehob that I spied, in a chaotic ironmonger's window, precisely the mantle I had been seeking for an ancient Aladdin oil lamp I have at home. When I asked the shopkeeper if I might buy it, he told me in a very weary way, "No, no. I couldn't sell you that. They're far too scarce. No. I cannot sell that. No." It did not seem worth starting a discussion as to whether he was running a museum or a shop, so I left. I found out later that these things are still made, are in plentiful supply and in widespread use in the more remote parts of Ireland. I put his attitude down to too much mud.

When you reach Ballydehob you have left behind the workmanlike market towns with their hideous traffic jams caused by car meeting lorry in a narrow high streets which was built just wide enough to enable ponies and traps to pass each other, while perhaps avoiding a man taking pigs to market by herding them down the middle of the road. In fact, these street have changed so little since those days, which are not all that distant, that as you sit behind a bus that is scraping alongside a fuel tanker jammed behind a trailer with a bullock in it that cannot move forward because there's another trailer with an even bigger bullock in it trying to reverse into a gap far too small, it would come as no surprise to see a haltered cow being led through the middle of the chaos, or a sprinting sow being chased by a boy with a stick.

Ballydehob is a bit different. Artists of all shades and talents, have made this their market town and centre of a new-age artistic community. Here you are more likely to be held up by a queue of traffic that stretches behind a woman delivering another kilnful of dismal pottery to a gallery, or a batik-maker carting a load of splodgy textiles, or a faith healer shopping for wholemeal bread. No wonder the ironmonger is tired of life.

Not many miles further, green meadows give way to rocky fields with thinner grass suggesting shallower soil. Rocks appear and you are no longer in a pastoral, but more of a foothill landscape. Indeed, you are at the foot of Mount Gabriel which stands guard over the fishing town of Schull. This town has changed too. When my wife and her family first set foot there thirty years ago, the only vegetables to be bought were cabbage, carrots and potatoes in sparsely stocked shops. Now the town is alive with delicatessen, supermarkets, bookshops, bistros and a bakery; but those who remember the old Schull say its heart and its head have not been turned by these contemporary trappings.

Schull is our gateway. Press on a few miles further, and we arrive at an even more peaceful place. I know of nowhere where you can travel back in time fifty years in a mere fifteen minutes; but you leave Schull with its Mercedes cars bearing Dublin number plates, smart yachts down from Cork anchored in the harbour, and six flavours of paté to be bought in the shops, and then be in a country where you are likely to meet a man hauling a milk churn to the creamery with a donkey and cart, or a family struggling to make hay in the damp climate with no more than pitchforks with which to fling the sodden grass in the air in the hope of getting some drying breeze through it. This is a land of wide views across the fringes of a changeable Atlantic. It is a coast where the crispest of clear air can turn murky and impenetrable in a instant, and the driving rain can soak you till you shrink. And all the time, Mount Gabriel casts its shadow; not in an overpowering or sinister way – these mountains have none of the craggy threat of the Scottish highlands. But it lets you know that you are standing on its toes by occasionally throwing up a massive grey outcrop of rock to spoil what would be otherwise useful agricultural land. It is no easy place to farm nor a convenient place in which to adapt to modern farming methods.

My mother-in-law fell in love with this place on her first visit and bought a romantically small and crumbling cottage on what is known as "The Prairie". This name is not a joke. Compared with the land around it, this fertile square mile that sits in a gentle hollow is devoid of inconvenient lumps of granite, thus making it probably the best bit of farmland between Schull and America. It was nicknamed "The Prairie" by the Somervilles who were the original landowners and the 42 acres have held the name. It is in the middle of this little oasis that John O'Driscoll farms, or at least used to. He has retired now with a pension and a few quid from the European Community to ensure that he never keeps cows again: Europe in general, and Ireland in particular, has too many cows. "Best thing I ever did! Givin' up. Best thing," he boasts as you meet him. But there again, there are those who will see his pace has hardly altered since he was working the land full-time.

Given that he and my wife's family are now firm friends, it is difficult to imagine that the early stages of the relationship between him and my mother-in-law were somewhat acrimonious. I do not know the ins and outs and only have the sketchiest of details handed down through generations, but at one stage in a dispute over who really owned the cottage, O'Driscoll threatened that as soon as her back was turned he would establish his territorial rights by turning his pigs into it. It is probably the only recorded incident of threatening behaviour, armed with a sow. They laugh about it now.

During the long spells of goodwill, the family would spend happy hours leaning over the walls of the sty, built of chunks of granite that once belonged to Mount Gabriel, scratching the pigs with a stick. My wife's brother Mike remembers going with O'Driscoll to buy piglets for fattening: "We went into this dark shed and John O'Driscoll struck a match which set all the piglets screaming. Then, while the match was still burning he quickly waved the light around the room till he spotted a piglet he liked the look of and shouted 'I'll 'av dat one'. Then he struck another match and searched for another. This went on some time."

Apparently, John O'Driscoll dislikes the water, which was unfortunate for a man who lived on a peninsula with the Atlantic Ocean effectively on three sides of him. Nevertheless, it was his practice to send a calf or two across to one of the offshore islands to graze for the summer. My wife was asked if she would care to row across to the island with her brother and an islander to collect the calf at the end of the season. Expecting to find a dear little animal with wide, brimming eyes, a velvety smooth nose and a body she could clutch to hers as they rowed the little creature, like Grace Darling, back to the mainland, she readily agreed. Alas, upon reaching the island, they found O'Driscoll's lack of aquatic courage had meant that the calf had been there rather longer than he had remembered and was now half way to being a full-grown bull. What started out as an imaginary scene out of Disney degenerated into recreation of Noah's worst moments when loading the Ark. The calf stayed where it was. All this servies to prove that farming in this far-flung corner of Ireland has its own unique form. In fact, my mother-in-law remembers that as recently as 20 years ago, the advice being given in the farming journals of the time – and fairly radical advice it seemed to be – was that pig food was best poured into a trough for the pigs to eat rather than be thrown over their backs for them all to lick off.

But do not believe for one minute that because Ireland may have been backward in its farming methods, it produced an inferior kind of pork. George J. Nicholls in his *Bacon and Hams* of 1917 notes: "Ireland has ever been noted as a pig-growing country, and for the last hundred years at least has sent bacon to the English market. In the year when

Queen Victoria came to the throne Irish bacon was sold in London in the retail shops of cheese-mongers, a writer of the time remarking that it was so well cured as to be equal to the bacon from any part of England, and was sold so cheaply that it provided good and cheap meals for the working classes."

I never met John O'Driscoll in the days before the flow of money from Europe finally lifted the Irish grassland farmer out of poverty and into undreamed-off wealth. Alas, it proved to be somewhat transient. Observers of the Irish rural scene will recall how families who were born to live in no more than hovels heated by a peat fire, would suddenly find themselves able to afford a smart car, and so outside the hovel would be parked the Mercedes. When the good times came to an end. the Mercedes went and all they were left with was the hovel, as if it had all been some dream.

The O'Driscolls have been smarter than that. What was a simple farmer's dwelling thirty years ago is now a smart little cottage with its new window frames, white paint and doors which do not hang off the hinges. It has all changed, except for the green wooden high-backed settle which still stands against the wall at right angles to the fire so that a chap may sprawl out on it when he is home from the fields. It was from here that John O'Driscoll and his wife Hannah spoke of pigs, ham, and of bacon.

"I gave up pigs 12 years ago. That I did," says O'Driscoll. "I gave up when the profit went down to a fiver a pig. I kept about 30. Pigs used to go up every week to Skibbereen but I always kept one back, yes. One a year to 'put in the tub' as we used to call it. We killed it at six months. I used to finish it on oats to sweeten the meat."

"Pigs like habits," says dark, wide-eyed Hannah. "They like to be clean and warm. Many's the time we've reared a piglet by the fire in a tea-chest. There was often a sow in every house, in rural parts." She leaned forward and her voice took on a more sombre tone, "There are certain houses . . this is country lore, this is .. . where pigs will not thrive. They just won't do. They die. So never be daring, because as soon as you replace the dead one, another will die. Ah, but they're delicate creatures. Ours lived in a piggery. Well, that was what we called it. I suppose it was a good as any of that time."

"When the pigs were ready," says O'Driscoll, "big Paddy Mcarthy from Dunmanus used to come. He stabbed 'em straight through the heart with a big knife and they bled to death." Hannah interrupted. "I was never allowed to watch the pig killing when I was young," she said, "but I remember that whenever we killed a pig we would give presents of pork to all the neighbours and relations and they would do the same when they killed their pigs."

The clock ticked loudly and steadily in the front room of the cottage. "We used to have lots of boiling hot water," said O'Driscoll, "we'd stick the pig through the legs and hang it up and then it was shaved with a razor. We tried to make a fine job of 'em, like. Then we got old timber porter caskets and filled them with strong salt and very little water, if any, and we'd put the hams in there, and we kept them moving. There was no running water in the country and so we had to make for the nearest stream when we wanted to wash the offal. Everything had to be scrupulously clean. I suppose fresh pork was a great treat for a while." "Yes," Hannah added, "it was a great treat, with cabbage. Sometimes we boiled the bacon with the bones and perhaps turnips. It was a truly delicious meal."

At this point there was an explosive statement from the lips of John O'Driscoll. His body quivered with enthusiasm for the statement he was about to make. Hardly able to contain himself and his passion for his food he declared, "I'd eat bacon and cabbage every day of the year. Every day! That I would! Bacon and cabbage! Every day!"

"You fry it in thick juicy slices," said Hannah, "with a bit of butter and then you sprinkle a tiny bit of sugar on it." "Thick, thick!" added John, "it has to be in thick slices. With a fried egg. And strong sweet tea. It is food to give you strength. Strength!"

There was a pause while we all reflected on the passion with which he had spoken. Then Hannah added, "I suppose to make it even better, you should have Bastable bread with it. A bastable was an old blackened pot that sat in the peat and the bread was cooked inside it. It was better than an oven because the steam stopped the crust from going hard." We sat and reflected upon this too. We spoke of the mingling of the flavours of the bread, the bacon, the cabbage. We grew fat on the mere thought of it. "Ah, but pork's not what it was," sighed O'Driscoll. "Not what it was since we stopped fattening our own pigs."

The O'Driscoll plateful is not difficult to reproduce, although to acquire the thick slices of belly bacon will probably mean that you must buy your streaky bacon in a slab from a butcher and cut your own hefty chunks. As far as the Bastable bread is concerned, you will need an open fire and a biscuit tin blackened by soot if you do not have the heavy, cast-iron, traditional pot. If you have no open peat fire, the recipe given in the 25th anniversary magazine of the Schull and Goleen branch of the Irish Country-woman's Association and submitted by M. O'Keefe will bring you acceptably close to the real thing.

Ingredients: 1 lb flour, 1 tsp salt, 1 tsp baking soda, 1 tsp sugar (optional), 1 pt of buttermilk or sour milk.

Mix all the dry ingredients together. Mix in enough buttermilk, to make a soft dough. Work quickly as already the buttermilk and soda are reacting. Knead lightly – too much kneading will toughen the bread while too little prevents it rising properly. Form into a round loaf, cut a cross on the top and place in a Bastable which has been rubbed with a butter paper. Place the lid on the pot, place on a hot turf or wood fire and pile hot turf on and round the pot so that the bread cooks from both sides. When almost cooked the lid should be removed, with a damp tea-cloth placed over the pot and the steam will keep the outside crust soft.

Nowadays a substitute for the Bastable Pot is a well-blackened biscuit tin with a lid. Bake in the oven for 30 – 45 minutes. When cooked it will sound hollow when knocked. Wrap immediately in a tea towel to prevent crust hardening. Gas Mark 8/450F/230C.

The bread is very popular throughout Ireland because it is easily made and it is often baked fresh for tea or breakfast. It is often called "Loaf Bread" when made with white or homeground wholemeal flour.

Before leaving the Prairies, I looked again at the piggery. It was indeed basic, but adequate and renowned as something of a local landmark. An elderly nun, Sister Catherine, a relation of Hannah's, made visits to the Prairie from her convent in England and was prone to forgetting the precise directions for finding the farm once she had left the main roads. She once hailed a taxi in Durrus and after driving around for some time, finally thought she had found the O'Driscolls. Just to be certain she asked the driver to wind down the car window. She stuck her head out of the window, took a deep breath of piggy air, and declared, "Yes! this is it". The pig sties are derelict now.

3

I find it difficult and somewhat shameful to admit, but I had little inclination to tour the south of England in search of my elusive ham. Which is ridiculous, for are not the great breeds of native pig from Hampshire, Wessex and Gloucester? And why should their hams be in any way inferior to those of the supposedly grittier North? I reminded myself that my own beloved Large Black pig is a native of Devon and Cornwall as much as she is of Suffolk and Essex, and they have hardly heard of her "up north." Nevertheless, for reasons that are entirely based on prejudice, I did not expect to find a ham or a bacon which would do justice to my (as yet unfulfilled) expectations. In my mind, pigs and pork were the fuel of the labouring man and I suppose it is a measure of the arrogance of the northerner that I still half-believe that no one south of a line from the Humber to the Mersey ever did a day's work in their life.

This is rubbish; but strangely, as I began to organise a circuit of the south of England, the face it presented to me was very much in line with my preconceptions. Here I was to find people approaching their pigs and their hams often as an artistic exercise; food for the mind as much as the belly. Here they can express feelings about their pigs, and enjoy the turning of them into food as a creative as well as a belly-filling exercise. It is difficult to put the finger precisely on it, but if I can draw an analogy with pottery; in the south they would be sculpting a delicate and precisely balanced teacup, while in the north they would be urgently turning out a mug from which to swill hot, sweet tea.

In Hampshire I met the Sutherlands, of Eldon; a couple who could only be doing what they do within a couple of hours drive of the appreciative taste-buds of the metropolis. I could not see them finding it so easy on the outskirts of Leeds. Sutherlands of Eldon, who are in fact Helen Sutherland, a refugee from the London advertising business, and Sam Olive, a slender, energetic and youthful chap who appears to be a refugee from life. He is a born-again pig farmer who farmed over

300 pigs in a conventional, intensive way until the big crash of 1983 when pig prices collapsed and farmers went out of pigs as fast as an unwilling sow flees from a farmer's grasp. Now, having tired of trying to follow the well-trodden ruts of conventional farming, he has become an innovator and invented a new pig, and by doing so has rediscovered an ancient one. But he has rediscovered more than just an old species, he has stumbled upon the old values of stockmanship and production of food.

To find him, *you* have to travel back in time. Head towards the West country till instructed to take a left turn off the dual carriageway and you will find yourself on one of the old A roads of Britain which were our transport arteries until the major bypass surgery of the 1980s. Now they are deserted and carry the levels of traffic associated with village lanes, while the major flow roars down their successors. But, strangely, they still have the infrastructures that lead you to believe you are on a major highway; vast garages that are hardly visited, white lines to segregate traffic at junctions where there is traffic no more. To find Sutherland's, we travel down one of these redundant roads till we reach Kings Somborne, itself a relic of the heyday of the small English village where ladies travelled on iron bicycles, the rector nodded to every passer-by, and Miss Marple watched from behind her net-curtained cottage looking for clues. But no clues yet to the whereabouts of Sutherland's, and their ancient pigs. So at the church we turn again and step further backwards in time. Here, woods and hedgerows still flourish, and pheasants and rabbits dart across your path with a confidence that suggests you are the visitor and this is their territory. The lane narrows and the trees thicken till you are in the midst of broad-leaved woodland; oaks and beeches dapple the sunlight as it falls on the lush undergrowth in which scurry animals and birds too speedy in their ways to be recognised. It is worth stopping the car to listen. It is not beyond belief that you might hear the ghostly trundle of the iron-rimmed wheels of the harvest wagon, and the thud of the horses' hooves on the road as they haul home the last of the harvest. Nothing can have changed down this lane for centuries; it would be a good place for old farming ghosts to take their exercise. And then we turn a corner and the vista widens and we go back another century as we look across a collection of small, fenced fields in which wallow Sam Olive's pigs.

These are like pigs I have never seen before. But there again Sam Olive is like no pig farmer I have ever met both in his thinking and the passion in his speech. "Anarchy! That is how I run this place. I ask the pigs what they want and we give it to them. For example, when it comes to feeding, do they want to be fed twice a day, with twice the stress of coming to the trough and ensuring their share, or do they want to be fed twice as much but all at one go? They decided on the latter, and that is the way we do it."

The pigs might be confused with huge dogs, at first glance. If dusk were falling and you were to come across this herd by accident you would fear for your life. But their anarchic regime leads to contentment and they hardly raise their heads as we walk past, which is strange given that their breeding is similar to that of the wildest of pigs that once roamed the ancient forests of England, but can now only be found foraging in the recesses of Eastern Europe.

Sam Olive has invented what he calls the Wild Blue pig, and it is just that. He takes one of his five wild boars (either Lech, Batori, Tambourlaine, Hitler or Mussolini) and crosses them with a sow which will have been bred from the crossing of a Large White, a modern breed, with a Saddleback, a rarish breed. It produces a glorious animal. One sow swayed towards us, udder brimming and sloshing from side to side, her litter following, all differently coloured. No dreary continuity here as modern pig production demands. "What we've done, by accident, is recreate the Hampshire Hog. I don't suppose the Hampshire Hog has existed for nearly 300 years but I happened to mention to a lady who knew about these things what I was trying to do and she said 'Oh, the Hampshire Hog!' It was an accident but that's what we've come up with." The Hampshire Hog was last found in its native county 350 years ago.

It is the ancient wild boar within them that gives Sam's pigs their long, pointed and powerful snout. The wild boar was a self-feeder who needed to truffle for his food. As we walked past a large open shed, a small herd of about twenty young pigs suddenly took fright and scampered into the corner, looking for somewhere to bury their heads. The feral blood, however dilute, was still in them. "These pigs have got the best of the old, and the best of the new," boasts Sam, "it's the ultimate hybrid vigour. When we started, there were no wild boars to be had, the only ones were in London Zoo and that's where they came from. But now they're imported. The leaner ones come from Poland, the fatter ones from Germany."

We walked up the field, divided into areas of about half an acre which might house a couple of sows and their litters. It is an open-air life with just a little shelter provided and plenty of grass for the sows to eat, which their wilder, foraging instincts say they need. "Modern pig farmers wouldn't even talk to me. They'd think I was some kind of New Age traveller or something for suggesting that pigs need grazing; but one of our big sows will get by on just a kilo of feed a day in the summer when the grass is growing. A modern pig would shrivel to nothing on feed like that." We pass a small field of pigs being fattened to ensure enough covering for the demanding charcuterie skills of a local chef. They are eating ground maize mixed with hot water, like polenta; no wonder the Italian chef prizes them so highly. They forage too, for acorns that fall from the oaks; a pannage as befits an ancient pig. "We've been spoilt. We just slice off the best joints and sling away the rest; but these Italians, they use the head and the ears, every bit they can. I'll tell you another thing. If you are choosing a pig to fatten, pick a thin one to start with not a fat one, because that way you'll get a better quality of fat."

These are sentiments rarely expressed by a pig farmer who is more often than not concerned about his piglets per sow ratios, his weight gains per kilo of feed, and all the other statistical jargon which Sam believes has nothing to do with producing good food. Sam Olive has bravely stepped outside that ideological prison, and his pigs and his produce are the better for it. We moved across from the fatteners to the boars. They ambled towards us, heads down like miniature hippos. Sam got down on his knees to chat. "When they first arrive on the farm I have my coffee breaks and my tea in the shed with them, just to get to know them." "Hello my darling" he murmurs, as a sow wanders over.

The boars are truly big boys, hairy "like a teddy bear in the winter", says Sam. The snouts, muddied from foraging, are as spiky as a porcupine, the dark ridge of hair along their backs reminds you of the markings of a donkey. "It is noticeable how the wild boar glides along whereas the modern pig snakes as she walks. That's because we've bred so much length into modern pigs and that's why they have all these back problems. Most of the problems with modern pigs we've created for ourselves. Our pigs take twice as long to grow to maturity as modern pigs, but it means that you get muscle that has matured properly – it's toned-up." The names of great chefs trip off his tongue; Koffman, Roux and others, all buy modest quantities of this most special of pig meats. "Everything in pig farming today is a five furlong sprint. It has all got to be finished as quickly as possible. We give our pigs *time*."

Together, we went over the familiar ground, we both agreed; the values of the old breeds, the sympathetic stockmanship that allows them their natural desires, the need for fat on a good bit of pork, and a general agreement that modern pig farming practices are an insult firstly to the pig. Then we had lunch.

I have rarely seen such a luscious leg of pork emerge from an oven. The crackling had gone slightly wrong, Helen admitted, but it was only a bit flabby and still looked delicious. The meat was shaded from almost white near the skin to a dark grey closer to the bone, a bit like turkey meat. The texture was silky, and the meat held together so it could easily be sliced thinly. It oozed with juice. She served with it an ideal combination of red cabbage- in honour I imagine of the pig's Eastern European parentage – and spinach. I went back for more, and more.

Given that I find so much common ground with Sam Olive, I was surprised to find myself sitting happily with George Streatfield. The two seem as ideologically opposed as two pig farmers could be. I found him in Dorset, in the famous Marshwood Vale between Dorchester and the sea, beloved of Thomas Hardy, and known for its luscious pastures which produce fine milk and cheeses. But forget any traditional, Hardyesque notions if you call upon Denhay Farms. As part of a partnership, George farms 1800 acres, milks 900 cows, employs 61 people and flogs 600 tons of his "Farmhouse Cheddar" cheese every year. Some farmhouse! Now he has big plans for his Air-Dried Hams and behind his serious, quick talking, hard-headed approach is clearly the notion that, one day, his hams are going to rule the world. He has gone into hams with the clinical approach of an engineer who believes that if all the nuts and bolts are in the right place, then you will have a machine that works. He has missed no tricks: he employed a food scientist to help create the secret formula for his brine, visited Italian prosciutto makers to gather intelligence, fostered marketing relationships with supermarkets. He *enjoys* hygiene regulations for the secure framework they give him and does not bat an eyelid at the many rules to which his buildings must conform. As a producer of pigs, he is not into sentiment or tradition but rears them in a modern, mechanised, efficient way which, all in all, adds up the sort of ham producer who has no place amongst the gallery of heroes I have visited so far.

But he deserves to be, for two reasons. His ham is of the best. At lunch we ate thin slivers of his Denhay Air-Dried Ham with fresh pear and avocado, and it could not be faulted in taste, texture or look. Every slice will be the same because George Streatfield is into continuity. But he joins my gallery of heroes principally because he has a pig product about which he cares, and it is truly special. It is a worthy rival to any Italian prosciutto. My only fear is that it may not last. His sights are set on big business and that means hands-off as far as he is concerned.

But at the moment, George Streatfield is an odd figure with one foot in the big time and the other in the brine tub. I explain to him that I find him confusing , a man to admire for his dedication and to despise for his industrial approach. "I am the meeting point of the two worlds," he explains. "Cows are what we really know about on this farm but we had to do more with what we'd got. I thought about Parma hams, did a bit of research and found they were the most expensive hams to buy and so decided to copy them. We went to Italy and went round two factories but I decided they did it best and there was no point trying to mimic somebody. So I hired a food technologist, who had started in the explosives industry actually, and began gathering technical expertise on how to produce prosciutto. I decided from the outset that the most important thing with our food was that it was safe. We went very carefully, starting with four hams a fortnight. My motto is: take it slowly, get it right, keep it right."

We went on a tour of the boning and brining rooms, wearing white coats as required by his "hygiene audit." He pumps the hams with brine ("I don't like the word pumping") to get an even cure through to the bone, but any injected fluid is of course lost during the drying process which can last up to a year. I asked him if he thinks of himself as a speciality producer or a small factory. " I think the word speciality has been hi-jacked. I like to think of myself as a supplier of food that's good to eat."

This has been proved, of course, by the success of his cheeses which have won many awards. In a link typical of a man who can spot a commercial opportunity a mile off, he deduced that the whey that would otherwise be wasted from his dairies could be made good use of to fatten pigs. "Our pigs eat wheat, barley, soya, vitamins, minerals and whey. It's a key part of the flavour." It's a fine flavour too, of that there can be no doubt. But whilst I would certainly not go so far as to say I had supped with the devil, for George Streatfield is a charming and hospitable man, I felt unease. It was simply too big; not my world. I cannot fault his hams but to my over-sentimental way of thinking, no man with an eye on the commercial main chance could ever cure a ham that would satisfy my longings. Ham is art. And so I went over the Dorset hills, not very far away, to find a haven in which I felt a little more comfortable.

For someone who respects, and can listen patiently to countryman's tales for hours on end, there is no better company than that of John Randall of Lytton Cheney, Dorset. Lytton Cheney is a village approached by a steep dive from a main road between clefts in the Downs that run to the sea. To drop into this thatched and tidy little community is to fall comfortably between the smooth breasts of Dorset and find a warm welcome awaiting.

Randall is an extraordinary countryman. Born in North Somerset, son of a wheelwright but associated now with Dorset and his beloved Dorset Down sheep, he has been shepherd, horseman and just about every other job demanded of the farm worker between the wars. He is respected too and sits on the committee of the Royal Smithfield Show ("they say the Royal Show sorts the men from the boys, but the Smithfield sorts the men") and many sheep breed societies are proud to have him as one of their number. He is a man of some dignity with a lengthy stride well rehearsed on the high Downs of Dorset, and on visits to London can be seen strolling from Waterloo station to his destination wearing his breeches, wide and flapping at the thigh, and leather buskins around his shins and ankles exuding confidence as if everyone else in the capital were somehow out of step with fashion. It is his proud boast that he has never sold a sheep or bought a sheep wearing a pair of trousers; a man must be dressed properly, he thinks, for the serious business of trading in livestock. These days, it is his sheep-trimming skills which are mostly in demand, for Randall can take a pair of sheep shears in his hand and within a quarter of an hour transform an indifferent looking animal into an award winner. It is widely said that if you want to win, Randall has to have trimmed your sheep for you.

But this is only a facet of his talent, and it was his days with pigs that I wished to recall; times when every farmer had a pig or two, and cottagers fattened one for their own use through the winter; when pigs, pork and bacon were part of the working family's life, and its guarantee of survival. Randall is as much a man of Thomas Hardy's times as he is of this century, for few of his values differ from those that were common 150 years ago. Except that Randall seems braver than some of Hardy's men. In *Jude the Obscure*, the village slaughterman fails to

45

arrive, and Jude and his wife are required to do the deed themselves. It is in sharp contrast to Randall's approach, as you shall see.

Jude, rope in hand, got into the sty, and noosed the affrighted animal, who, beginning with a squeak of surprise, rose to repeated cries of rage. Arabella opened the sty door, and together they hoisted the victim onto the stool, legs upward, and while Jude held him Arabella bound him down, looping the cord over his legs to keep him from struggling.

The animal's note changed its quality. It was not now rage, but the cry of despair; long-drawn, slow and hopeless.

"Upon my soul, I would sooner have gone without the pig than have had to do this!" said Jude. "A creature I have fed with my own hands."

"Don't be such a tender-hearted fool!"

John Randall started young and so was never going to lose his nerve in later life.

"I stuck my first pig at fourteen. I was on holiday at my Uncle's and I came down one morning and the copper was boiling away. I worked out what was happening. I said 'I can't hold a pig!' Uncle Harry said 'Never mind, you can stick him.'" Randall's bright eyes water with excitement as he tales the tale, "I was bloody frightened to death but you grew up quick in them days. What we used to do was this: Uncle Harry and Uncle Lew, who were both big men, used to stand across the pig, grab it by the earholes, and lift it. That was a 10 score pig mind, not a little thing. We used to put a rope through its mouth to hold it. Then I stuck it. You go in . . ." he mimes as he talks, and pauses to heighten the drama a little, well aware that by modern standards where all pig-killing is done behind closed and sanitised doors, this is shocking stuff, ". . and down. The cut has to be about three inches long, and four or five inches deep. The idea was to cut the main artery, you see, and then the pig bled to death. 'Course, there was no stunning or anything beforehand like there is today but I'll tell you, they died quicker then because the heart was still pumping the blood out. They were stone dead in less than half a minute. Mind, you had to collect that blood if you wanted the make black- pudding, catch it in a bucket and keep stirring or it congealed. The greatest crime when sticking a pig was if you twisted your knife 'cos you could easily spoil as much as a pound of shoulder meat and then there'd be hell to pay!"

These were the days when no farm was without a pig, especially on the grass-growing lands of Dorset. It was common practice, Randall explained to me, for a farmer and landowner who did not wish to dirty his hands with the labour-intensive and demanding task of milking cows, to let his pastures and dairy to a "dairyman" who did all the work. Much of the milk was made into cheese, the whey being a waste product of that process which, fortunately, pigs were only too happy to devour. That was how every farm came to have a pig or two. "Very often, they made more out the pigs than they did out of the milk. That's true. We used to kill 'em on a Saturday, put 'em in great big wicker baskets and put 'em on the train at Bridport, 6 pm on a Sunday. They'd go up to London, be sold Monday morning and the baskets would arrive back empty a Bridport station on a Wednesday. Could you imagine British Rail doing that today?" he chortled away.

Randall had now gone over to his desk and started to search deep into drawers. What emerged, clasped in his hand, was a grim reminder of a regular farm task. It was a knife; "stuck hundreds o' pigs, this has." It was now little longer than a dinner knife but in its heyday had been a lengthy piece of steel. Repeated sharpening had ground it down till it was almost a spike. "Cut like a bloody razor, this would. Hundred years old." The blade was not straight, but curved slightly upwards and the short wooden handle, smoothed by the firm and sure grasp of the slaughterman, was held by three hefty rivets. "It was quick . . ." said Randall, weighing the knife in his hand, ". . . no messing." And so that's what you used to stab them with? I asked. "Not stab, stuck! We *stuck* pigs."

"The favourite pig round here was a Wessex Saddleback sow crossed with a Large White boar. Every farmer had enough of his own pigs to fatten; they bred everything of their own. They didn't buy pigs. Any amount of people kept pigs, fed 'em on taters, scraps, barley meal. Of course, it was dying out but the war brought all that back."

The next stage, after the killing and the bleeding, is the butchering which cannot start till the pig has first had its hair removed.

"We allus used to scald 'em. Some people burned 'em. What we did was to take a butt-barrel, a big 'un about one hundred and twenty gallons, and cut it off two feet high. We put about fifteen gallons of water in it and about one and half gallons of cold. Now, you had to be sure the water was the right temperature 'cos if it were too hot you'd blister the skin and then you'd have to burn the hair off. If it were too cold, it wouldn't come off so it had to be dead right. So to test it, you took about a teaspoon of blood and dropped it in the barrel and if it frothed up like a atomic mushroom, the water was too hot and you added a bit more cold. Then you get a hand crook, do you know what they look like? I'll show you, I've got one out the back, and you put it in the pig's snout, pull its legs round and put its arse in the tub, then pull its head round till that was in the tub. After a minute or two, you tried scraping at it with a sort of candlestick, do you know what they look like ? I'll show you, and when the hairs started to slide off easily, you lifted its back legs up, and dropped its head in. The head was the worst part to scrape, all fiddly round its eyes. You had to keep moving, mind!"

Listening to this rapid-fire narrative, it was impossible not to feel the urgency with which all this had to be carried out. If any step was accomplished with less than the required speed it was clear that the process could become a tortuous nightmare. Strangely, I found it compelling and not at all gruesome. After all, the pig is dead and must be dealt with efficiently out of respect if nothing else. It had laid down its life for you and you must honour its memory by ensuring that everything it has to give is not wasted.

"It was promotion if you were allowed to help with the dressing. After all the hairs had been scrubbed off, you opened up its tendons and pushed what we call a 'gamble' through them. You open up the throat a bit, just by the side of the windpipe, and tie a bit of knot in its gullet so that the contents of its stomach don't fall out when you turn it upside down. Then you pulled its back legs apart, hung it up, and opened up the belly. You cut round the bum," Randall twists an imaginary knife in his hand, "about four or five inches and then you gently insert your hand behind the cut, and cut down. You must not cut the gut or all the muck will come out. You go down as far as the ribs and then all the guts come out and you have to go back to the liver, and heart and lungs."

Then it was the turn of the women. Randall pointed to the fast-flowing stream that ran alongside the lane outside his house. "Then you had to wash the gut. The women did that. There'll have been thousands of pig guts washed in that stream out here. They used to push 'em onto a stick and wash 'em and then when you pulled'em off they turned inside out, see? Then you soaked them in salt and water for a week."

Great memories, I said. "Yup," said Randall. " Last time I did it was . . ." he paused, "couple of years ago I suppose. Bloody great boar it was." Then we had supper. Steak and kidney.

This was not the first time I had eaten here. A few years ago I trawled through the rich seams of his farming memories searching for his reminiscences of his days with cart-horses. On that occasion, I had called at lunchtime when his wife had served the most delicious brawn I had ever eaten. Brawn, something of a memory of childhood days when my grandmother went on endlessly about its virtues, was one of those things which I felt eventually I would grow into. Now, at John Randall's table, my time had come.

His wife had made it, and on this return visit I determined that I would extract the recipe. They recited it almost as a duet so I cannot distinguish one from the other, but it goes something like this;

"First of all, quarter the head, You've got to have the ears off and the snout off – too tough. You need a big pan of boiling water and a teaspoon of salt and you boil the head till the meat comes off the bones. You need to put some pickling spice into the water. The whole lot – you boil up the brain, eyes, tongue, everything. When it's all boiled and while it's still hot, take all the meat out but leave the eyes, and the skin, and you don't want too much fat. You have to skin the tongue and tongues don't skin very well so you have to sort of razor it off. And then you chop it all up, put it in a bread tin, pour the juice over it, and add some water that's got some gelatin in it, and put it in the fridge to set. And you must have the jaws, the bath chaps, the lower jaws of the pig or it won't be much of a brawn."

Here, the conversation paused while I took all this in, and then they mentioned, in a slightly hushed voice, "Of course, faggots are better." Faggots? I asked, and we were into an other recipe.

"You need the whole of the pluck of a pig; the liver, lights, heart, kitcher and veil." I was none too certain about these last two. After some discussion we decided that the kitcher is probably the pancreas. "Now you take all this and you don't chop it – you mustn't do that – you mince it. It takes ages, and needs a good knife. Then you put it in a bowl, mix it with some bread crumbs till it holds together, add a bit o' salt and parsley and thyme. Then you have to take the veil and spread it out and then roll up your faggots in that. All you have to do is bake 'em. Put a drop of oil in the bottom of the pan. They'm beautiful!"

The delicious nature of the steak and kidney, and the talk of the brawn and the faggots, took us back to talk of hams and bacon.

"You know," said Randall, "the brine was the easiest way to cure a ham. Mind, the brine had to be strong. You had to add salt to the water till it was just strong enough to float an egg, put your ham in there and let it stay for a week or ten days. Hang it up to let it drain, put it in a muslin bag and that would last about 6 months if you kept it somewhere cool."

I asked if they hung it up the chimney, to smoke, like real farmhouse hams were supposed to hang?

"Up the chimney to smoke! Old load o' rubbish that were. The reason they hung 'em in the chimney was so the draught could dry 'em. Nothing to do with smoke at all." We ended the evening on a good laugh.

It was from Roger Keen that I was to glean yet another piece of vital advice, should I ever be contemplating the purchase of a south-country farm. "They always used to say, hereabouts," he spoke from the yard of his own farm just to the south of Chippenham in Wiltshire, "that if you want a fertile farm, buy one from a cheese-maker." I found this a confusing piece of logic at first, but he explained. "Cheesemakers always kept pigs which they fed on the whey which was surplus to requirements. There's nothing so good for fertilising the land as pigs, so buy a farm from a traditional cheesemaker."

Roger Keen, whose business is called Sandridge Farmhouse Bacon, strikes what I would consider to be a nice balance between business, farmer and ham producer. "We're not organic. I think a lot of that's silly. We employ what I would call sensible husbandry. We've got 300 and grow about 500 tons of wheat and barley all of which is fed to the pigs. We've got seven working on the farm, and seven on the bacon." Keen, a short and animated man, talks fast and furiously about his bacon, pausing only to insert inverted commas by waving his fingers around certain phrases as he speaks to express either disapproval or scepticism, and he is sceptical about a lot of things.

"All this used to be built out of wood," he said, pointing at his curing sheds now built of dreary plastered blocks. "We've got to 'keep somebody happy'," the fingers wagging around the words. Clearly, here is a man who has felt the full force of over-zealous inspectors and in the subsequent match seems to have achieved a draw where others have suffered ignominious defeat. "I'm a farmer first; farming is what we do. But we always used to cure two or three pigs a week. Of course, Wiltshire's famous for its bacon. How it came about was because pigs were shipped over from Ireland and landed at Bristol docks, years ago. They were then walked, yes *walked* towards London. What happened was that by the time they got to Wiltshire, those in charge of walking the pigs would do anything to get rid of some of them, so they often got sold for tuppence, and that was how the Harris Bacon factory started here in Wiltshire." This all seems unlikely, but it is true. In 1770, John Harris and his mother opened a butcher's shop in Calne, which was a resting place for both pigs and swineherd on the long march to London and Harris was able to buy pigs very cheaply this way until the Potato Famine of 1847 put an end to the export of pigs from Ireland. By then, however, his business was well established and in the process of seeking a supply of pigs from America, he discovered the technique for building ice-houses which meant he could cure hams all year round instead of, traditionally, only those months with an "r" in them. As factory bacon and ham production goes, the rest is history.

Keen slid back the door of his chiller and I was confronted with a sight that was becoming all too familiar in my travels, but one that never failed to gladden my heart. It was the glorious spectacle of mahogany hams, glistening with salt and slightly dulled by the mould of maturity, hanging patiently, drying and improving in flavour with every day that passed. A heady scent invariably cascades from the hams as the chiller door is opened, and in the frostiness of the air hangs the sweet smells of smoke, ale or molasses; a salty tang which could almost deceive you into thinking you were beside the seaside.

Keen has five cures for his hams. There is the Brumham: "a coal black rind with a ruby red centre." The Devyses: "rich flavour of the hops coming through." The Trubridge: "rare, preferred by those with a delicate palate." The Chipnam: "Deep pink, firm when cut." The Golden Rind: "recreating the essence of Inglenook smoking."

We walked down the trays of hams, patiently curing in their trays, and sniffed at the ones submerged in ale, or treacle. Keen told me of the juniper berries, the boiling beer, the cochineal to give colour, the black peppers. He described the smearing, the tossing, the turning, the loving care and attention.

He opened the door of an old transport container and we stepped into the smokehouse. This was like stepping into a mediaeval dungeon licked by the flames of hell. The base of this steel container had been cut away and a foundation made of concrete and bricks to prevent the spread of any fire, and a small hole had been cut at the top of one of the walls where it met the roof, to provide a rudimentary chimney. Rays of sun entered the smoky chamber through this tiny hole and one could imagine a felon gazing from the blackness of this cell at the shafts of light piercing the remnants of the last smoking, praying for release. I shivered.

"Do you know," said Keen, "the 'health inspectors' (the inverted comma fingers were waving in the air again) wanted me to clean this out after every smoking." We looked at the heavy tar deposits on the walls, the charred sawdust, the hinges of the door thick with ash. To cleanse this rich vessel of smoky odours would have been as sacrilegious as scrubbing out a mature tea or coffee pot. "We use oak and beech sawdust," said Keen. "We put straw down the middle and light it and then it burns away. We let the hams hang for two days and we dampen it down if its going a bit too quick. It can get quite dense." I told him that I had heard that in some factories, they reproduced the effect and the taste of smoking by painting onto the hams a chemical that must be a close relation of the one that gives smoky flavours to crisps. He looked at me, confused. "I don't know much about factories. They're all controlled by financial considerations."

We emerged from the smoke-hole and wandered past more trays of hams curing in rich, red brines the colour of claret. "There's lots of bacteria in here, all working away. They're helpful, we like to think."

Then came the pigs. Largely for show, I suspect, were Gloucester Old Spots; one living in the most romantic of bricks stys with an curved arch over the doorway and a convenient oak tree overheard so that acorns fell directly into the sow's open mouth. But the commercial pigs, all bred and finished on the farm, were kept in as reasonable conditions as a commercially kept pig can expect. They were housed, but had plenty of room to roam, and shelter for privacy and change of view. They seemed content, and so did Roger Keen. I went across to his farm shop and bought bacon, smoked sausages and ham and was just about to leave when I came across a packet of heavily breadcrumbed Bath Chaps. I had never seen, let alone tasted, a Bath Chap and I had heard of them as being a great delicacy. When Bath was a Spa town and all manner of classy parties were held there, the Bath chap was considered a smart thing to have for a late supper. It is no more than the cheek of the pig, cured, cooked and rolled in breadcrumbs, and the chaps from Bath probably came from the local Gloucester Old Spot pigs which had long jaws giving a chap of a decent size. They are considered a little fatty for modern tastes. But since contemporary tastes in pork are no part of my philosophy, I looked forward eagerly to Mr Keen's Bath chap. I left Sandridge Farm thinking he was a decent sort of chap too, and put him high on my list of contenders of those who can be trusted with a product as special as our native hams.

Later, I tasted the chaps and did not care for them. They were too rubbery by half and as my jaw moved up and down on them I felt, rather too strongly for comfort, echoes of the similar movements the chaps themselves must have made when they were still in working condition. But this is probably a fault of mine, and not Mr Keen's. I had never tasted a Bath chap before, and like so much of the pig which does not come from the leg, shoulder, belly or loin, it is an acquired taste. But the half pound of Brumham Ham I bitterly regretted was not half a stone; it was exquisite. It was not a floppy specimen of flaccid, pink flesh; but a meat with body, texture and a sweet flavour that set every taste-bud alive. The rind was black, and chewy, and a little went a very long way. I was very glad to have met Mr Keen.

But one vision still haunts me from my brief tour of some of the southern counties, and here I must introduce Klaus. Klaus is sixteen years old, and luckily, very dead. All that remains of him is his head, stuffed and mounted like a hunting trophy on the wall of the office of Nigel Dauncey. Dauncey's name was mentioned to me by Sam Olive as a source of wild boar. Having been mesmerised by the distant sight of those primitive, dog-like boars of Sam's, I wanted to know more.

Dauncey's Somerset farm gives no hint that anything ancient or unusual may be going on there; the only clues being the stuffed head of Klaus, the founding boar of Dauncey's small empire, and an odd telephone conversation I overheard while waiting in the outer office. It went something like this; " Crocodile is nice . . . yes, it comes as crocodile tails . . . about 2 lb on the bone . . . yes, peacock is very nice too . . . tighter texture than turkey . . . nice gamey flavour to it. I'll send you our price list." You will have gathered that Dauncey is not merely into exotic pigs. Later, he was to take me into his chill room to examine a couple of bison.

It all started with wild boar. "We are so far behind in this country," he says. "There are over 1,300 boar farms in France. I started in 1984 when milk quotas were first introduced. We were a dairy farm with a commercial herd and like everyone else, we started panicking. I tried growing asparagus, and then someone mentioned wild boar. I approached a zoo to try and get some breeding stock, and wildlife parks too and eventually I got hold of a boar and three sows. It was all seen as a bit of joke to start with. We got small litters and they only bred once a year. Eventually I got hold of some French stock, and then a couple of German boars. Do you know, every country in Europe except the UK, Ireland and Denmark still have wild boars? It's 350 years since we had the last wild boar here. I remember some Polish pigs we had," he laughed at the thought of them, "well, it took us three weeks to catch them. We made a sort of race and moved them further and further down it by teasing them with food. Unmanageable they were. We put up a fence eight or nine feet high but they just launched at you, trying to clear the fence." I pondered on that placidly featured, stuffed head of Klaus, and thought rather differently of him after that.

I asked if there were any virtues in these pigs, as animals. "There aren't any virtues at all! It's a much better meat and lower in cholesterol as most wild animals are. But that's it. As breeding animals, they've got nothing going for them whatsoever." We walked over to a heavily fenced field and spied a group of boars, resting in a far corner, sitting and sniffing the air as a jungle animal might when sensing predators. One of the boars rose. "We won't go any further," said Dauncey. "When they get aggressive, their hair stands on end and the idea is to make them look bigger." Their tails were already thick, standing erect. I thought of wart-hogs. Then another rose to its feet, and sniffed in our direction. Time to say goodbye.

There is no doubt that there is something hypnotisingly primitive about these animals. Here we were, in the most rural part of Somerset, and we could equally have been on safari. The feeling of peering in on animals that were unfamiliar with the ways of man was particularly strong.

It would have been a common sight in Britain three centuries or so ago; but the forests were cleared and the ancient practices of feeding pigs on what they could root for in woodlands gradually died out. Cheesemakers discovered they could fatten pigs on surplus whey and arable farmers found they could feed them potatoes. The pig came in from the cold to the sty and has never been the same again. But here, in the south, the potted history of the pig can be observed within a radius of twenty miles. At its most modern at George Streatfield's embryo empire, Sandridge Farm lies a decade or two behind him, John Randall extols the virtues of pig-keeping as it was practised during the first half of the century, Sam Olive goes back a couple of centuries further by bringing ancient blood to modern breeds, and Nigel Dauncey is back where it all began.

4

I breathed the luxurious and heavily-scented air of the duty-free shop at Vienna airport as if it would be my last breath of free air for ever. I eyed the salamis and the air-dried hams, but my mind wandered. Quite frankly, I was terrified at the thought of the next leg of my journey. For God's sake, it was only to Romania; but it was as far east as I had ever been, and to what I expected to be a strange and hostile land where the old politics of oppression were lying in wait to entrap a simple chap like me. And Vienna airport, with every western luxury from liqueur chocolates to goose-down duvets, seemed so safe and comfortable. Why should I be searching the departure boards for a flight to Timisoara; a town that provided the spark that lit the bonfire of the revolution on which Ceausescu was eventually thrown? Why not stay here, have a nice strong coffee and a slab of creamy chocolate cake, as one does in Vienna, and then go home?

I suppose I am not a very confident traveller. As I lumbered reluctantly towards Gate B10, I started to eye up my fellow journeymen to try and get the measure of those poor souls who were heading in the same direction. Of course, Vienna is an ideal place to let the imagination go into free fall. As any thriller reader knows, it is crawling with imagined spies. Consequently, I was certain I had identified several agents; the fact that they were reading the *Financial Times* was just a blind, I thought. Then, hoping they might be chaps from some innocent teacup factory in Stoke-on-Trent who were heading east to try and put Spode on the Eastern European map, I tried to start a conversation but got a mouthful of German for my efforts. It would have been nice to have had a like-minded, little British businessman to share my worries with, to talk about the weather, or the price of things in the shops. But there were only Germans, Austrians, and what I assumed were Romanians. The latter were easy to spot by their shoes. Shoes, I am told, are an international give-away and porters at smarter hotels can often tell the difference between the gate-crashers and the residents by their footwear. The Germans and Austrians, I noticed, wore highly polished and sculpted sheets of leather; the Romanians seemed to have wrapped their feet in sheets of shiny cardboard destined to fall to pulp if they got wet. I was wearing Marks and Spencer's imitation Doc Martens having decided that they would look smart enough in any situation, and handy if I had to plod farmyard tracks, or kick doors down, or kick-fight the Securitate, or . . . I looked over my shoulder as the coffee bars disappeared into the distance and the faces of my fellow travellers grew sterner as take-off approached.

This, of course, is wimpish behaviour of the highest order. I was being met at the other end by a couple of cheerful, English-speaking Romanians who had visited Suffolk the previous year. I had met them, liked them, and when I spoke of my interest in pigs they had told me that anyone who could, owns a pig in Romania. Music to my ears.

It had always been my intention somehow, to observe the pig in its rightful place, which is at the very heart of a peasant culture. Over a large part of Eastern Europe, the pig still has the status that it once enjoyed here in Britain a century or more ago. It remains a cheap source of food which can be preserved through the long, cold winters. It is an animal that can be butchered without waste, and fattened on minimal amounts of cheap food. It is a walking, grunting support system; a lifeline where supplies of food are either not available or cannot be afforded. I very much wanted to see the pig, still at the centre of peasant life, and observe how the pig is cared for, killed, and cured. Romania was as good a place as any to do it.

In fact, it was probably better than most countries I could have visited. To a Westerner's eyes, this country has been a heap of trouble for most of this century, and probably much of the last. To take just the last 60 years; they have had a royal dictator, a fascist Iron Guard, joined Hitler's invasion of Russia, been defeated and ended up being invaded by the USSR themselves. The King abdicated and a People's Republic was established which attempted to move away from Russian influence, and in 1964 declared itself totally independent of the USSR. In 1965, Ceausescu came to power and proved to be one of the great bastards of the twentieth century, pursuing not only crazy notions but bloody ones too. Abortion was banned, and family planning too, because he believed that the country's prosperity depended on the size of the workforce: more kids meant more workers meant more economic success. Of course, the vast majority of the population, who were still wise peasants at heart, knew that this was claptrap and that

56

the only way of securing prosperity was to keep a pig in the backyard. That way, the Pig in his Palace in Bucharest could do what he liked, they would never starve.

And so the pig-owning, peasant culture has survived in Romania. There are no quick and ready meals to be had from supermarkets, salami is in the shops but at prices that few can afford. Is it any wonder that a pink, fat pig in the backyard represents prosperity in a country which has little else? I boarded the propeller-driven aeroplane, fastened my seat belt, and decided that if the pig can live with all this, surely I can survive it for a week.

By good fortune, the central European air that day was clear and cloud free and I had a fine view as we left Austria, flew into Hungary, and out the other side. I was heading for a town called Salonta which sat not many miles from the border between Hungary and Romania and stood out like a pimple on the vast, flat and fertile plain between the Danube and the Carpathian mountains. The nearest airport, at Timisoara, was a couple of hours drive away. The moment we crossed the border was evident from the change in the texture of the fields. All this land looked rich and black from the air – not unlike the Fens of Lincolnshire – but in Hungary, where the country is more advanced and ridded itself of communism that much earlier, the farming is of a higher standard and so although both countries farm their huge fields in strips, the Romanians seem to do so less neatly and their field boundaries look like the unravelled edges of a cardigan.

In the distance, I could see a smallish town and the outline of a concrete runway. The small plane banked steeply, came in to land, the doors opened and we stepped onto the tarmac. I took my first breath of damp and chilly Romanian air. A rag- bag of soldiers surrounded the aeroplane, their hands on their guns for no reason that I can imagine. We were kept in a tight group till we were given the signal to stroll over to the decrepit terminal building which seemed to be holding together by good fortune rather than design. The soldiers, having accepted that none of us seemed a threat to the fragile stability of their country, started to mime the rapid smoking of cigarettes in the hope that we might throw them a few fags, as bones might be hurled to starving dogs.

Then came the long, slow queue at immigration where the officials are chosen on the basis of how threatening they can make a half-closed pair of eyes. They fiddled, stamped, checked us out on their screens, and with the greatest of reluctance let us pass. The customs officer wanted my bags opened and found, much to his disappointment, only books for my hosts. I suspect a few boxes of fags or booze might have gone astray here, had I been carrying any. I cannot say the first impression of Romania was a welcoming one, yet it was not overtly threatening either, just glum. I was glad to see Romi waving at me from the other side of the barrier.

I settled myself carefully into his car, for I figured that any sudden jolts might cause vital parts of it to drop off. It was a "Dacia"; a Romanian version of a Citroën, I was told. Romi, a schoolteacher in his mid forties and full of enthusiasm as well as good English, drove me instantly to the cathedral steps in Timisoara as if it were the only thing to do. In pouring rain we gazed at the bullet holes in the buildings where the army had attempted to crush the revolution, and failed. We stood at the memorial to those who had been killed and stumbled over gypsies littered around the square (much to Romi's disgust). Gypsies are loathed in Romania, despite representing ten per cent of the population. In many parts of the country they are merely itinerants and pose no particular problem, but in some villages they run Mafia-like operations and are hated. Decent people, like Romi, do not give them a second look.

Travelling with Romi was Nollo; a swarthy, Latin-looking fellow with black, greasy hair and a brownish complexion. Nollo spoke little English and seemed subdued and hardly enthusiastic about standing on the cathedral steps in Timisoara, celebrating the revolution.

Through the incessant rain, we gazed at the Opera House, nodded briefly at the other sights in this crumbling little town and with dusk falling headed out of Timisoara on the most dangerous road I have ever travelled upon. It is a major highway linking Timisoara with Oradea, the principal town of Bihor county, yet it has the dimensions and construction standards of an English country lane. It is perfectly straight, and flat, (this was a Roman country for nearly two centuries from AD 106) which makes it dangerous. The temptation to overtake is great and in Romi's car, where brakes seemed an occasional luxury and the connection between wheels and steering a tentative one, the fact that the seat-belts did not seem to connect with the body of the motor-car became a worry. This road carried not only massive lorries and tankers which straddled the centre of the road, hedging their bets, but the occasional horse and cart which carried no lights and loomed out of the dusk causing us to swerve, often into the path of one of those wandering lorries. I ticked off the kilometres to Salonta, and prayed.

Nollo, sitting in the back did not seem much worried by any of it.

On the bridge at Arad, there was a crash of glass followed by a thump. We found that a headlight had dropped out and the thud had been caused by our running over it. Romi shook his head in despair, no doubt calculating that the cost of a replacement would be half of his week's wages. He is headmaster of the school in Salonta with over a thousand pupils from the age of eleven upwards but his status and efforts gives him no more money. To become headmaster you are elected by your colleagues and if you don't want the job, tough luck. No extra pay either; not even a few extra lei to buy nuts and bolts to secure headlights.

Driving across the flat plain at dusk was like being at sea. There were no features with which to judge our position and from the distance came the occasional flicker of village lights, like passing ships in the night. I could see the vague outline of haystacks, and mountains of freshly cut maize, and I swear I could smell the occasional pig as we sped through a village. And in the twilight, huge red tractors belched filthy smoke as they ploughed using non-reversible ploughs of a type which were phased out in Britain nearly 30 years ago.

"Pigs," I said to Romi, "have you fixed for me to see any pigs?" I asked this question rather tentatively for I had written them a full letter explaining that my reason for coming was to immerse myself in their pig culture. I was worried that this might be viewed as an irrational request by someone who was really coming on holiday but had been too shy to say so. I was relieved when he told me that Angela, his wife, had "fixed a very full programme. Pigs every day!" he chortled. Nollo did not smile.

Had I not known in advance that Romi and Angela were charming and hospitable people with whom I knew it could be a pleasure to spend a week, eventual arrival in Salonta could have been depressing. It is not a large town, but the outskirts are attractive with single storey villas painted in earthy reds and browns reminiscent of the colours and textures of the buildings of Siena. Horses and carts were common in the side-streets, even after dark, and until we arrived in the centre where Romi and Angela lived, it looked a perfectly pleasant little spot. But God, those blocks! Those hunks of concrete that Ceausescu directed be built to a pattern laid down by the Russians! You could not sit down and draw a grimmer facade, nor construct a building that was going to age and disintegrate as quickly as these hovels. They had no hint of softness or welcome about them; doors hung off hinges, skips

59

littered the untidy yards, and in the centre of the courtyard stood a smallish factory-style building, the boiler room, providing hot water and heat for up to 30 blocks in the vicinity. A rusty, broken-down boiler had been dumped outside, and the loose panes of glass rattled in rhythm with the roaring of the oil-fired furnaces. I thought of the fires of hell, and what a hell of a place this must be to live.

But I changed my mind. Romi's flat was clean, warm, tidy, comfortably furnished, and although the stairways did smell a bit of cabbage and leaking gas, there is no doubt that far worse could be found on many inner-city housing estates in Britain. In fact, although the infamous blocks are without doubt an architectural eyesore, and many ancient buildings including churches were demolished so that they could be thrown up, those who live in them do not complain, much. They were built, I was told, to house the peasants and farmers who fled from the land after Ceausescu collectivised the farms. He took not only all the farmers' land into common ownership, but he nicked the livestock and produce as well. Demoralised, the farmers came into the towns, looking for work. To satisfy them Ceausescu, being the sort of fat-head whose hare-brained schemes could be faulted by any averagely intelligent school-child, built any old factory he could think of on any old site he happened to choose. That is why Salonta now has an abandoned textile factory. The fact that you can only produce textiles if you have an abundant supply of water seemed to have escaped the inspired planners and their dogmatic leader, and so the factory was doomed before it even opened. Later in the week, I was to see another textile factory built on a site not unlike that to be found in the middle of the North York Moors. It was all as crazy as building a car factory in the Scottish highlands.

But the legacy of all this was the blocks. No one who has any choice in the matter prefers them, but the ones I visited were reasonable, if small. All are said to be privately owned now. The big dream is to build a house of your own. Before the revolution, no one dared buy a plot of land and dig foundations for if the state suddenly decided they needed the site for something else, you were evicted without compensation. The notion of a complaints procedure did not flourish in Ceausescu's day.

The room in which I slept, piled high to the ceiling with books, spoke volumes about Romi and Angela. To my shame, all the great classics of English literature which I had never read were here, some in English, others in Romanian translation. I lay on the bed, which space dictated should be of the fold-out variety, and gazed up at Aldous Huxley, Bertrand Russell and T.S. Eliot. Through the window came the noises of the main street echoing off the walls of the blocks: the clop of horses' hooves and the gentle hum of traffic. Close the eyes and you could imagine you were in a seafront boarding house in Britain, overlooking the promenade where ponies and traps were taking trippers on a circuit of the sights. But these horses were, although not in poor condition, only adequately fed, and hauled narrow wooden waggons piled high with maize, or hay, or sacks of meal which the farmer had just collected from the mill. Even though it was a mildish November, the drivers (both men and women) were heavily wrapped against the cold air, the men preferring a black triangular hat, the women a sheepskin cap. I looked out of my bedroom window to see an ancient and hardly threatening armoured troop-carrier slip through the town. Salonta is only three km from Hungary and the town now has army protection. On the basis of what I saw, there was not enough armoury to stop an insistent pussy-cat, but one glance from my window gave me a distillation of my first impressions of Romania: army, peasants, horses and blocks. It was suppertime.

I hoped it would be pork, but in fact there was never any chance that it would be anything else. There is no other meat to be had here. There *are* cows to be seen in fields and so there must be beef. I saw sheep too, so somewhere you must be able to buy lamb. But Romi and Angela are desperately hard-up, like most of the people in their country, and so it was the faithful and self-sacrificing pig that came to their rescue as it has done for generations the world over. We had a sour soup to start. Angela had spent many hours in the kitchen, as all Romanian women seem to do, preparing food. Nothing processed can be bought, at least at prices anybody other than the very rich can afford. "We have no choice," she told me, "we just get in the kitchen and cook." She always closed the door: the kitchen was not man's territory and husbands were not expected to help. Actually, one gets the impression that husbands rarely offer, nor children. Romi, their son of fifteen, did not even know where the matches were kept, or how to make coffee – it was woman's work. The sour soup was, well, sour. I imagine it would have fallen more easily on the palate of someone who relished sauerkraut, that rather acidic, central European preserve of vinegar, salt and cabbage. Given the mix of European blood (stretching from the Yorkshire Moors to the Urals) which flows in my veins, I should have relished sauerkraut but I have always found it the most repulsive and slimy mess whose acidity ties my stomach in tight knots. I knew, however, that it was part of Romanian cuisine and so in preparation for this trip I had braced myself for many plates of sauerkraut.

But the sour soup is nothing as bad as that and is made by frying sliced onions till they are transparent, adding a little salt and paprika and pieces of pork, mostly on the bone. This is something else to which you must adjust, for most cannot afford to cast aside hunks of pig simply because they might be fatty, gristly, or contain little more than joint tissue. It is assumed that every bit of the pig has some goodness in it and so deep within any plateful of Romanian food may appear the oddest of anatomical specimens.

Once the bones have been added, cold water is poured into the pan, with salt and pepper if necessary, and the whole lot simmered until the pork is cooked or falls away from the bones in resignation. At this point, the sourness is provided by a small glass of vinegar.

You should now blend a couple of spoons of flour with sour cream till you have made a paste, and pour this into the sour soup. It then boils till it thickens. It is quite delicious, and was my first taste of Romanian food. Good, nutritious, cheap grub made with what most people would have had to hand: pork, onion, vinegar, cream and flour.

We had a plate of mashed potato about which I thought very little until I toured the shops later in the week and realised what an expensive luxury this was. I now wish I had been more grateful, but spuds are just spuds. Instead, I looked at the table hoping that something green would appear but for the duration of my stay this was to be a futile hope. The only thing that is fresh, green and readily obtainable in the winter is the cabbage; but that is stewed to a pulp in almost all the cooking. I developed a taste instead for the pickled cucumbers, some preserved in salt, others in vinegar. And I took a fancy too to the pickled mild paprikas, red and juicy and almost sweet which I had eaten in Britain and believe them to be called pimentos. They are not to be confused with the fiery, small and potent red paprika which will blow your head off at the slightest taste.

A plate of sliced pork arrived, simply fried till it was nicely brown. And then cabbage leaves, with rice and meat. Actually it was sauerkraut, warm rice and meat, which made it even more acidic. This dish is not unlike the sour soup and made by slicing onions, frying them and adding pieces of pork, salt and paprika. The sour cabbage is added when the meat is half done and then both cabbage and meat are cooked till tender. You then add sour cream. I enjoyed it, I really did.

It was new, it was Romanian. The company was good too, and so was the wine which was white and Romanian and would surely have enjoyed a good export sale, but it was explained to me that after decades of insularity the idea of selling abroad was not only new and alien, it was a notion to which large sections of the population were positively hostile.

But, oh, the *tsoica* was another thing completely. There seems to be no ban on the distillation of spirit, as we have in Britain. And so in Romania, where autumn plums are plentiful, a clear white spirit is made by the distillation of fermented fruits. It smells of plums but the spirit is so strong (verging on the petro-chemical) that to the novice drinker unprepared for the toxicity, tongue and palate are paralysed, the throat scorched upon contact. There was always *tsoica*, everywhere, every time, whatever the time of day, whatever the occasion. Any excuse was taken to swig a measure of the stuff to keep out the cold or dull the senses to the reality of life.

When supper was over and Angela proudly paraded her packet of Earl Grey obtained on her only visit to Britain, and offered to make tea. Instead of the Earl Grey, I suggested she try a little of the strong English Breakfast Blend which I had bought at Vienna airport partly as a present but also for selfish reasons having guessed, correctly as it turned out, that after a day or two away from home I would willingly kill for a cup of English tea. The tea-making ritual was a sight to behold, and a painful experience for a serious tea drinker. She put the leaves into a small kettle, added cold water and brought the mixture to the boil. She then poured this brew through a strainer into a large teapot adding "I remembered to warm the pot, as you do in England." The resulting fluid was perhaps a little strong, and a bit stewed, but any assessment was difficult because to it was added boiled milk. The boiling of the milk, I was told, was essential because there were no regular supplies of fresh milk and so it did not figure in their diet. But in my honour a bottle of milk had been bought at the market. Angela told me that it came in an old Coca Cola bottle and the contents were still warm when she bought it suggesting the heavily clad lady who had sold it to her had removed it from the cow not many minutes previously. Angela thought boiling it was essential, but being unskimmed whole milk, thick globules of fat floated to the surface and these she had to skim before adding the residue to my tea. All in all, with tea scarce and the milk dubious I was pleased when she produced a tin of instant coffee which was drinkable black. The making of tea was clearly going to be more trouble and more costly than it was worth.

As the *tsoica* coursed through our veins and loosened tongues, the conversation turned to politics as it seemed to after most meals. To be able to talk freely is a new-found freedom for them. The revolution happened as recently as 1989 and until then, foreign visitors were rare in this part of Romania. Indeed, if foreign visitors were expected the secret police, the Securitate, had to be informed and a note taken of all conversations that took place between the visitors and their hosts. If the Securitate did not like the tenor of the conversation, I imagine walking down dark alleys was to be avoided. Terrifying an entire populations by the use of a secret police force is a ruthless and cunning way to run a country. As was explained to me, no one had any idea of who the secret agents might be. "After the revolution," said Romi, "we wanted a list published but no list was ever produced." Amazingly, when the identities of some of the secret officers were released, a close friend of theirs who regularly came to play cards was found to be a Securitate agent. I imagine the things he heard in Romi and Angela's flat would have turned a committed communist's hair grey for they were both fluent in the hatred of the old regime. "He promised us he never informed on us," said Angela, "but just knowing he was an agent now makes us sick." Angela had once been hauled in front of the secret police for having received some suspicious novels from the USA. These had been opened by the Securitate and it was found that one of the dust jackets used the Nazi swastika as part of its design. It was an innocent enough book about the war as anyone of reasonable intelligence and education would have realised, but Angela was summoned to appear before the secret police to explain that she was not a Nazi wishing to overthrow the regime. "I had to go to Oradea. They make you sit and wait for hours. Thick set men, leather coats, black glasses." Then she spat. I asked what happened to them after the revolution? "Oh, they are running things now! They were always paid very well so they had the money. They are businessmen. Yes, doing very well."

I asked about pigs, of the grunting kind. I wanted to know what had been planned. "We cannot go to the mountains, to the Orthodox villages, because we are in the middle of the church's pre-Christmas fasting period and nobody kills pigs. But here in Salonta we shall see a traditional pig-killing day, and visit villages too, to see pigs." I went to bed, Dickens to the left of me, Huxley to the right, Ceausescu's roof above my head, and pigs in my dreams.

Breakfast proved a little tricky for I came immediately face to face with the unpalatable truth about how pork is eaten here. I was offered "a little bacon" and was not prepared for what appeared on my plate. If you imagine bacon to be a pleasant blend of meat and fat, the meat being in the majority, you would not recognise this stuff. It is no more than the whole of the back fat, with the meat *removed*. It is just fat, nothing else, salted and possibly smoked, and with a texture that clings to the throat as every swallow inches it further towards an unwilling stomach. No amount of heavy bread could force it down and I was saved only by the arrival of the instant coffee. I looked closely at the slab of fat, not believing what I was seeing. But, of course, when you have a winter to survive and have lived in a country where the heating of your home was a fairly random affair under the old dictator, you sought your energy supply where you could get it, and as in so many fundamentally peasant cultures, the pig provided it. Personally, I would rather have melted the fat, stuck a wick in it and huddled round the flame. But I put a brave face on it, swallowed hard, and declined bacon thereafter.

I was given a whistle-stop tour of Salonta, a town typical in that like most towns in Romania it is still getting over the shock of no longer being under communist rule and is coming to terms with alien ideas such as the free market, and making money. Desperate for a coffee, I suggested Romi and I might call at a coffee bar. This was a new establishment, run by young people attempting to imitate the ice-cream parlour style that is beamed to them by satellite TV from the west. The furniture was cheap, the newly painted walls were already looking seedy because the paint was such poor stuff, the coffee was cold. I was offered cream with it, which given our conversation of the night before about the poor supply of milk should have set alarm bells ringing. The cream was some whipped chemical concoction which floated on the cold, strong and bitter coffee like a slick of diesel on a puddle. Thank God I did not bother to buy an ice-cream. "This is all new," said Romi, proudly. Indeed it was. The other shops in the row were a mixture of newly opened food shops selling a good variety of provisions, but at prices few could afford. The remaining shops were still the property of the state and their invitation to buy was all too easy to refuse. Plump old ladies, huddled in shawls, perched by a till which was next to a wood-burning stove, like hawks waiting for someone to dare enter their grim little nest. The wooden shelves were bare and unpainted and offered large tins of pickles, or jam, and nothing else. There are few grimmer prospects than a state grocery. And all the time I was there,

Romi and Angela reminded me of how much better things are now. "I no longer feel humiliated when I go shopping," said Angela, "now I have the choice of what I want and what I can afford. I am not ashamed to ask for what I want. We have bananas now, for example. Until a couple of years ago, my son had never seen a banana." The fact remains, a pound of bananas costs a third of her week's wage of about ten pounds. I suggested I change some sterling into Romanian lei and was shown the local currency exchange. In this small shop sat a heavily made-up and coiffured young lady with a shiny leather bag and not very much to do other than sit by the large green safe which she never seemed to open. Scribbled on a sheet of paper and stuck in the window were the exchange rates and we figured that about 2,800 lei to the pound would be about right. Tomorrow it might be many more with inflation at over a 100 per cent. Instead of disturbing the woman's peace, Romi suggested he would change my currency for me. I thought this might be a great trouble for him but, on the contrary, he was most insistent. Back at the flat, he delved deep into a cupboard and emerged with a fat wad of notes wrapped in a brown paper parcel. He counted out 50 quids' worth, which was about his month's wage, and sensing that this was a considerable sum to him and not very significant to me, I decided that I would spend my money cautiously and resist the temptation to buy up half the town, which could easily be done on an average British wage. Of course, he was more than delighted to have the sterling, and would have been even happier had it been Deutschmarks for, he told me, anyone with savings is not foolish enough to keep them in the ever devaluing lei; instead they get it into one of the world's hard currencies as fast as they can, often bought on the black market. The smart thing at the moment, apparently, is to sell your house for Deutschmarks if you can, for if there is a gap between the selling of one house and the buying of another, the lei can depreciate at such a speed that you end up being hardly able to afford the garden shed, let alone the house of which you have dreamed.

We paid a brief visit to the school where Romi was headmaster. I looked at the clean and bright, but chilly classrooms where the 1,200 children from the area around Salonta are taught. Romi's first job of the day is to supervise to spreading of waste oil on a mountain of scrap timber which has been collected from around the town. The school's boiler is designed to run on oil but this is usually in short supply. Romi's next job of the day is to go and argue for more fuel, which is usually not forthcoming. Angela teaches English here, struggles to enthuse them about Dickens; in particular, *Bleak House* figures largely in their comprehension text books but they do not have a single copy of *Bleak House* in the school, or *Tess of the D'Urbervilles* with which the students also have to struggle. But they have an unlimited supply of western pop culture beamed at the them by MTV, the European pop music television channel, and on the day I visited them a disco had been hastily assembled in the school yard and was blaring 60s Beatles music to the kids who jogged around as much to keep warm as anything else.

Back home in the block, lunch was swift swig of *tsoica*, a glass of sweet red wine which was said to be Ceausescu's favourite and with which we once again toasted the demise of the old bastard (and which Romi mixed with Coca Cola in what must be the cultural clash of all time). The food was the warmed pork and sauerkraut from the night before. It was still acidic and the sharp edge to Ceaucescu's deceptively sweet wine did nothing to neutralise it. Even though it was lunchtime, talk turned to politics, "The people here may be poverty-stricken," declared Angela, "but they will not work because work is beneath them. Under communism they never had to work. Now they do not want to. It is the youngsters in the school that I worry about. All they want to do is get out of this country. But they are our future. New York is their dream." For the next day I was promised less politics and more pigs.

Before the pigs, one more supper which was to reveal something of the mysterious nature of Nollo, the man with whom I had shared the car from Timisoara and who lived in the flat above Romi and Angela.

He turned out to be quite a nice guy and any reservations were entirely due to his manner which was silent, grim, Balkan mixed with a little dour Russian. Nollo thought the revolution had been a bad thing. He was a communist and pined for the communist days. No wonder he had been less than delighted to be on the cathedral steps in Timisoara. He and his wife, who presented us with a lavish plate of salami, more sour soup, more pork with cabbage, and for a change a gloriously cooked hare marinaded in wine, had recently been to Bucharest which is a major undertaking on an uncertain railroad when you are travelling from Salonta in the far west. They brought back with them snaps of the great palace that Ceausescu had been building for himself; a cliff-face of a structure with marbled rooms so huge and ornate that no one can now imagine what to do with them. In order to build this vile celebration of his absolute authority, Ceausescu bulldozed some of Bucharest's finest buildings, including the oldest church in Romania, and countless houses and communities and ordered thousands to work on this self-congratulatory project. The loss of life was apparently huge. Now it is an eyesore and an embarrassment. But Nollo and his wife thought it spectacular; "It is as wonderful as Versailles," she said, "and bigger!" Angela nearly choked on her salami in anger. "We never discuss politics with them," she told me later, "they are nice people, but communists." Talk turned to England and the images of England that had become instilled in these Romanian minds. "Ah, Bobby Charlton," sighed Romi's brother, who was at this small party. He then recited the entire England football team that won the 1966 World Cup. "Your Tom Jones," said Angela, "is a very powerful singer, marvellous." The conversation edged towards politics again. They are completely unable to avoid the subject. It is as if they have been witnesses to an horrific accident, and need to talk it out of their system. Romi had advised me that supper parties in Romania always follow the same course. "First nobody speaks and everyone drinks. Then, everyone speaks and everyone drinks. And then everyone speaks and nobody listens. Always politics!" The conversation came round to inflation and I mentioned that Britain had its worst inflation sometime in the early seventies. The name "Harold Wilson" came up and Nollo, his little left wing ears tuning in to the conversation for the first time, miraculously and with great excitement burst forth with the dates of every Socialist governments Britain had ever had. He hadn't bothered to learn the Conservative ones.

Nollo turned out to be principal of the Salonta Agricultural College and hoping to see the very latest in Romania's pig farming, I persuaded him to show me round the college and farm. The building, on the outskirts of Salonta and lying past the salami factory, not far from the abandoned textile plant, had for a period been taken over by the army, so we passed what appeared to be a military checkpoint complete with chequered barrier in order to get as far as the innocent car-park. In the classroom were cabinets displaying models of typical Romanian farming equipment which would have been worthy of a museum display in this country. Not that any of it would not work and perform the tasks asked of it; it was simply that this was a place of education and you would not expect a modern school teaching metalwork, say, to consider the bellows as an item of equipment to be found in a modern forge. We went to Nollo's office, a high ceilinged and rather stately room with a nail in the wall where he clearly hoped he might one day re-hang another picture of an even more glorious communist dictator. He opened the drawers of his desk and pulled out two bottles; "vodka or plum brandy?" he asked.

After yet another swill of the *tsoica*, Nollo explained to me that things in Romanian farming were really going quite well; they had good crops and had adequate fertilisers. Some of this may be true, but I was warned by Angela that the old communists had been brainwashed into never saying a wrong word about the state. Everything, they were taught to believe, was going well and it was deeply unpatriotic to suggest to a foreigner that anything was running less than smoothly. However, one or two things I knew to be the case: the Romanians are working hard at re-organising their farming now that the land has been de-collectivised and given back to the farmers. They have no machinery and cannot afford to buy any and so they contract their farming work out to the remaining state farms who have the machines they need. But the state-owned machinery is a monopoly and the prices that are charged are way beyond what most farmers can afford. Those far-sighted individuals who have a spark of initiative in them are forming cooperatives and buying machines of their own, but these are few and far between. The Government has said that these farmers must be offered low interest loans to purchase their machines, but the banks are not interested in lending. "But even if they buy the new machines," said Nollo, "people do not know what to do with them. Nobody wants to come and learn farming. They think they've got the land and don't need to be told how to use it."

Lest you think that Nollo heads some thrusting and modernising school, it is worth describing the school's farm. Like everything in this part of Romania, it is approached down a pot-holed road that had a murderous effect on Romi's already battered Dacia car. Dusk was falling as we left the school and headed in the direction of the Hungarian border where the school's farm was situated. This vast plain is a miserable place on a grey, drizzly night with dusk falling. It stretched as far as the eye could see, the horizon not broken by any tree, and the only feature on the landscape was the rising smoke from a distant bonfire. After a stirring 15 minutes of dodging pot-holes and parades of horses and carts returning unlit from the fields, we arrived at some low, whitewashed building on which, in flaking letters on a mucky white-washed wall, one could just make out that this was the school's farm.

We went first to look at the cows. Nollo told me that Romania had two native breeds one of which is a brown cow with white marking, and the one from the north of the country is brown all over. They also have milky Holsteins. We stepped into the cow shed, and backwards 50 years. By the dim light of a low-wattage single electric bulb, one man was slowly working his way along 20 or more cows, milking by hand into a galvanised bucket. I asked if they had a milking machine. They told me they had one once, but it broke and there was no money to replace it. Anyway, they got on quite well milking by hand.

The pigs were a mixed bunch. They imported breeding stock but the pure breeds did not do particularly well in the Romanian climate due either to the hot summers or freezing winters. Generally, I was told, they found them most useful for mixed breeding. There was much Landrace blood evident in the long white pigs, and some gingerish Duroc too. But the litters were small in number and size and there was no evidence that the intensive methods of breeding and fattening pigs, which rule the roost in the west, had gained any ground here. Barley meal was the staple diet, and by the hessian sacks of meal lay scythes and hooks which are still part of the college's tools for daily use. As we left the college farm, I noticed a recently erected safety poster. It described how to safely harness a horse, and what to do if it bolted.

Before making our way back to Salonta, we crossed the road and called on a young chap who represented the very few who are working hard at seizing new opportunities. He had a small patch of land, a good

fertile couple of acres, on which he had built polythene tunnels and in which he was growing vegetables, and paprika, and trying hard to make himself a living. He had a shed close by his tunnels in which he stored his bags of crudely manufactured fertilisers; and in the corner was an iron bedstead, a stove with a kettle on it, and a television He explained that if he did not live here night and day, with his big-toothed dog, his crops would vanish and his tools would disappear. "Gypsies," explained Nollo, never willing to admit any fault in his fellow countrymen, who he dearly wished were still communists.

Slowly I was getting nearer to the pigs and the pig-keeping culture I had come to see. I was being tantalised with the promise of a traditional pig killing which was still a couple of days away. But on my first Sunday in Romania, we piled into the trusty Dacia and coughed and rattled our way out of Salonta on a bright and breezy November day, heading for the village of Talpos (*pron.* Talposh) ten miles away. The roads are straight and long and disappear over the horizon. They are interrupted only by the occasional junction which crosses the main road always at right angles. The villages are built that way too; the roads intersect to form blocks just like American towns, and the roads are wide, have no tarmac, and are steeply crowned so that water can run freely from them into the wide ditches on either side. In these ditches, flocks of geese amble around the village indignantly hissing at anyone who might try to disturb their foraging. They spread themselves across the road too but have practised the art of dodging traffic which never seems to slow down. At precisely the moment you are certain that old Mother Goose is going to disappear under the wheels of the Dacia, she does a quick flip and emerges, crossly hissing at the intrusive car. The odd pig was to be seen too, gently truffling its way along the grass verges, snout down and moving earnestly forward bent on capturing every morsel of food. None of these itinerant flocks or herds seemed to have a home, but I was assured that every creature knew its home and would return safely before dark. The only time that problems occurred was when the farmer decided to paint the farm gate during the day. This, apparently, caused endless confusion to the baffled pigs and especially to the geese.

I was to be a guest of the Gruia family. Petru is an inspector at the local salami factory and he had arranged to show me as many pigs as I wanted to see in the village of Talpos. But first he showed me his father's aged bright blue truck which, it was explained to me, represented a major entrepreneurial investment on the part of his family. Most farmers in Talpos rely on a pair of horses and a flat waggon on which to cart produce from field to market. The ownership of a truck was huge leap forward, and the sight of such a vehicle in the village was something of a rarity.

Apart from the geometrical layout of the villages, I was also confused to find that all those who lived there seemed to have two houses. Take the Gruia family. I was shown into one house, darkly furnished with deep-brown wooden furniture, large cushions, and heated by a wood-burning stove as large as a decent sized cupboard, free-standing and covered in glazed ceramic tiling. This radiated heat with the efficiency of a nuclear power station approaching melt-down. But when I was given a tour of the rest of the house, it became clear that although it was clean, it was cold and unlived in. We were brought coffee, and the most delicious of vanilla slices, from the small kitchen. Then we strolled across the yard which was shut in with a high, solid metal gate as were all the yards in this village, and I was then shown another house, this one clearly lived in and where we were going to eat lunch. Two houses: one stately, for show and entertaining; the other a worka-day establishment in which life was regularly lived. Curious, I thought. Romi explained that all families started with one small house and gradually extended it until it was as large as they wanted it. Then that one would be mothballed and kept for special occasions while across the yard another would be built. Still very curious.

Then we took a stroll to see pigs, and more pigs. There was not one house in this village which did not have a pig, or two. All pink pigs – "we call them York pigs" – and housed in a clean, tidy and sturdy sty not far from the house. As it was November, most were well grown and plump and ready for killing. I met all kinds of farmers, most of whom had dressed in a grey or navy-blue suit in honour of my visit. I was proudly shown their yards in which they keep their golden and pre-cious heads of maize for the winter, and their stacks of sweet-smelling lucerne hay. In a shed, there was usually a cow or two, and a pair of horses munching at hay. Sometimes, the farmer's wife would appear in traditional long dress, head covered. "The villagers are very proud of the *big* pigs," Romi translated for me, "they often have a competition for the biggest pig. Everyone here has a pig. Pork is their main food. They have two main breeds of pig which they call the Large White, or the White York and a couple of Romanian breeds called the Bazna and the Mangalitza. These are usually good breeds for reproduction."

All the faces of the older people I met in my wandering around Talpos showed the marks of long hours spent on the fields under the scorching sun. Hands too showed the marks of manual labour. None of these villagers owned tractors themselves but hired state-owned tackle to do the ploughing and cultivation for them. Before the revolution, none round here had land of their own. All was collectivised into huge farms, some having a thousand cows. After the revolution, "everything was shared out, even the bricks from the buildings."

I met one old man who was so revelling in the post-revolution freedom that he had gone back to work to enjoy the feeling of working for his living rather than being handed it on a plate. "When everyone owns everything, "he complained, "no one cares about anything because they do not think it belongs to them."

One farm sticks in my mind. The elderly couple who run it were bursting with pride that someone from England should want to come and see it. As had become the practice, I was given a tour of the show-house first, which was neat and freezing cold and unlived in, then I was taken into a cool damp cellar when bottles of preserves lined the shelves. There were pickled plums, cherries, jams made from peaches, hams drying in the chill breeze, sacks of flour. I was startled by this display which would rival any presentation a supermarket could offer and, sensing my enjoyment, a huge, weighty glass jar of cherries in syrup was hauled from the top shelf and thrust into my arms. I explained that I had to return to England by plane and such a thing could not be carried. But this was an alien notion which they were never going to understand. Having learnt not to refuse Romanian hospitality, I negotiated my gift down to a jar of peach jam and was very grateful to have it.

Thinking I had seen the entire establishment, even down to a tour of the earth closet which all the houses had, I was then taken into the tiniest and darkest of rooms, in which roared a wood stove pumping out heat into a confined space that housed a high double bed built like a box, so that it had to be climbed in to. There was a table and two chairs, and that was it. This was where they lived. They had two, fine, comfortable houses, but preferred this cosy little cell. I must say that I did too. Out came the *tsoica* and as the alcohol seared through me and the heat from the stove worked its tranquillising ways, I could see how easily one might hibernate in this little hole for the entire winter, till the pickled plums and *tsoica* ran out.

It was late afternoon by the time we hauled ourselves out of that

cosiest of hovels and made our way back to the house. Lunch was prepared by a mother figure that I had not seen until now for she had been
slaving in the kitchen as is the lot of all Romanian women of her generation (nor is there much evidence that things will be any different for
the next). Father had made the wine from his own grapes grown on
lines stretched across the yard in which stood his bright blue truck.
The wine was fruity, sweet, but not too sweet to be enjoyed with fried
slices of pork, the inevitable sour soup and the sauerkraut. I took one
more hefty swig of *tsoica*, loosened my belt, and settled down with a
hunk of heavy bread in one hand and a chunk of fried pork in the other
for my fifth pork dinner in three days. Flocks of sheep ambled slowly
down the main street as dusk fell, and as promised the geese seemed
to find their way home. Only an odd pig or two were left wandering,
but they had that look in their eye that said they too were thinking of
home.

Angela announced to the assembled gathering that tomorrow was
going to be a traditional pig-killing. "Ah," they all shouted, "and will
Paul be eating the ears and the tail?" with a mischievous curiosity
which gave me the first hint that the next 24 hours might be quite hard
work.

I slept fitfully that night, curious as to what the dawn might bring. In
fact, it brought a cold, frosty morning and a cup of instant coffee. It
was half past six and we were urgently piling into the Dacia, having
promised we would be at the pig-killing at seven sharp. We made an
urgent diversion to a "non-stop" 24 hour shop, a new phenomenon in
Romania. It seemed to me they were just there to tantalise the population even more, for if they could not afford anything between nine
and five, what would come over them in the middle of the night that
might make them able to afford a bottle of cognac? Romi bought a
dozen cans of beer and with a wipe of his sleeve on the windscreen of
the frosty Dacia, we spluttered through the darkness to the outskirts of
Salonta. We were heading towards the home of the Panti family,
Rodica and Misu. Misu has his own mill which presses sunflower seeds
to extract the oil. Some of the oil he sells on, some of the pressing is
done on behalf of local farmers who pay for the use of his press and
take the oil away for their own use. I had paid a quick call there when
I had taken a stroll around Salonta on that first morning. I had slithered on the oily floor between the sacks of seeds, seen the horses standing patiently while the waggon load of seeds was carted in sacks, and

brought out, crushed, in cans. I had also seen the pigs, living in a slippery but fattening world where the residues of the crushing process, a greasy, gritty paste, were tossed towards them and made them grow exceedingly fat. This was clearly quite a thriving business and explained why Misu lived in some style in a small villa. Even so, he kept a fine pig in the backyard which was separated from the vegetable garden by a stout fence to save the pig from temptation. Rodica told me that in the garden she grew tomatoes, potatoes, radishes, cucumbers, cabbages, parsnips, carrots, beans and peas. "Everyone who has a garden," she told me, "grows their own vegetables."

We went first to the kitchen where everyone was slowly gathering, Misu having clearly just risen from his bed. Sitting in the corner, bearded and with a woolly hat pulled down over his head was the butcher, Alexandro, complaining that we were late. The killing and the butchering of pigs, you must understand, was not his profession; he was a carpenter by trade and this was his hobby. Between early November and Christmas, five or six pigs a week would fall to one swift stab of his knife and his urgency was based on long experience. He knew that the preparation of a whole pig from stabbing to complete transformation to food for the winter would take most of the day.

We left the kitchen having swilled strong coffee on empty stomachs and strolled to the yard where the pig lay innocently in its sty. A large black, hairy hound called Tommy leapt at us from behind the wire mesh cage in which he was kept, and his barking split the still air of the town. He paced, leapt, barked and generally sensed excitement. Alexandro deftly grabbed the pig by its hind leg, slipped a loop over it and tied the pig to the gate so that despite any struggle, it could never regain its feet. Then he stuck it. His knife went in, was twisted to sever the main artery, and withdrawn. The pig's eyes briefly glazed over, in shock. Even Tommy stopped barking for a moment. Then the blood started to pump and bowls were brought by the women to collect it for the making of the blood sausage later in the day. The pig got over the shock of being stabbed and started to squeal and struggle some more, irritated that its hind leg was still held captive, unaware that the very life blood was pulsing from it. The more it struggled, the more the blood flowed till slowly but surely it slipped into an unconscious state and was declared dead. It took a quarter of an hour. The pig did not look pained, just confused.

There was no moment of requiem, or sorrow, or begging of forgiveness for what they had done. Instead, a flagon of *tsoica* was brought from the house and glasses handed round. Stiff measures were poured and the pig toasted. The party had begun.

By now, the women had retreated to the kitchen, which they knew was their rightful place, and from the kitchen could be heard the clattering of pans and the hissing of kettles of boiling water. Tommy, the black dog, was now in a frenzy as the corpse of dead pig was hauled towards a mound of straw which was to be its funeral pyre. The idea was that the burning straw would singe the hairs from the pig before butchering. As it was lit, a golden glow filled the still dark air of the dawn and with another glass of *tsoica*, we toasted a fine pig that would see this family through the winter.

When all the straw was burnt and the dead pig had taken on the colour of a Christmas pudding, Tommy the dog became nervously quiet as he realised that the pink pig was now the same colour as him. Then the scraping began which would turn the pig pink again. With a long-bladed razor, Alexandro shaved the creature with as much care as a barber tending a valued customer. It took most of half an hour before the entire carcass was shaved as smooth as a baby's bottom. The blood had long since ceased to flow and dawn was breaking on a scene which could not have changed in centuries. The cock crowed, the chickens that wandered around the yard came and gave the dead pig a quick glance and clucked off again. The church bells rang out and with a swift slice of his knife, Alexandro removed two hunks of pig meat from the top of the front leg and threw them into a pan which Angela had brought from the kitchen. This was to be the basis of breakfast, which was still a couple of hours away. In the meantime, Alexandro had a smoke to gather his strength for the butchery. "I like a castrated pig," he explained, "otherwise the pork will not taste good." His knife was hard at work on the pig's penis which disappeared deep into the carcass and which Alexandro spent many minutes extracting. "You can eat the testicles," he declared, "if you know how to cook them." The penis was thrown at Tommy the dog, who again went strangely quiet. For all his apparent keenness to get his jaws into some pork, this bit did not seem to take his fancy.

Misu climbed into the loft and threw down strings of home-grown garlic which were taken off to the kitchen where the women sat and peeled them. On the kitchen table, the pig's blood was cooling in large bowls. It took a strong stomach to drift from kitchen with its pungent garlic odour and the smell of solidifying blood, to the yard with its odour of freshly opened pig guts. I took another swig of the *tsoica* largely for its anaesthetic value, and looked at my watch. My eyes took time to focus in the half light and I realised that I was well over the limit. It was only half past eight in the morning.

Having slit the pig down its belly and carefully allowed the intestine to fall into a washing-up bowl, Misu called another halt for a cigarette. "There are few left now who do it this traditional way," he complained, "they all want to do everything quickly. Speed, speed. But if you go into the villages all the old people know how to do this. They don't have to have someone like me to kill the pig for them." We gazed down at the stomach, lying on the floor. "The stomach is very good," he said, "filled with tongue and kidney, garlic, pepper and salt." With *my* stomach churning with the *tsoica*, this delicacy took some imagining.

Empty pans started to emerge from every cupboard in the house, bright red and green ones, enamelled and large enough to qualify as catering rather than domestic equipment. But these are in regular use during the pig-killing season and clearly worth the investment. The church bells chimed again, the chickens grew braver and edged towards the offal intent on pecking the trimmings from the liver which had been intended for the cat. "The bacon is very fine," declared Alexandro, slicing a huge slab of fat from the back of the pig. Then, the moment came. A swipe of his knife removed an ear which he then peeled, and sliced, and passed round with a pot of salt. In the bravest act of my entire life, I took a piece, dipped it deep into the salt hoping that it would gather sufficient to completely mask the taste, and then I took a bite. Children came running from the house to share this delicacy and tucked in with the relish a western child might consume a Mars bar. "I shall send the other ear to my father down at the mill," said Misu and his children hastily ran down the road with grandfather's treat. I thought I was going to be sick. It was, I imagine, like chewing someone's dead finger: fleshy, gristly, unbearably salty and tough. I could not swallow it and fell back on more *tsoica* to swill it down. I thought I might take refuge in the kitchen.

This was a mistake, for the thick slices of neck pork were just hitting the pan of water and the air was filled with the smell of boiling meat and the cabbage which was in the pan next to it.

I retreated to the yard where at least the air was fresh and found Romi and Misu trying to light a boiler in which they intended to stew the heart and lungs and some of the solidified blood. But it was so cold that the gas in the bottle would not vaporise so the canister was dipped into a bucket of hot water and suddenly a huge flame sprouted from the burner and the water started to bubble. Alexandro was tackling the pig's feet. Misu tried the hinds and struggled, but Alexandro had them off with a deft blow. Misu, who spoke no English but watched satellite television and so knew every Western commercial product by its advertising slogan, grabbed hold of the trotters, held them high in the air, and shouted "Adidas!"

It was now eleven o'clock and time for the first feast of the day. Breakfast was declared. We left the carcass which now looked less and less like a pig, and went into the house to be confronted by a groaning table laden with chunks of heavy white bread and crispy, golden slices of pork that had earlier been cut from the neck of the pig, More *tsoica*, wine or beer and then came pickled paprikas and cucumbers and a dish of molten dripping in which to dip the bread if the pork itself did not have enough juiciness about it. This was truly a great feast and the pork as sweet and perfectly cooked as any I have eaten. Alas, I failed to realise that this was merely a curtain-raiser to the serious eating that was to come later in the day. I dare say I over-indulged. But never mind, it was a great feast enjoyed by all and we agreed that the pig did not die in vain. "Well," said Alexandro the butcher, "three hours from now we shall be done, then we shall have the sausages made, and the sour soup." He leaned back as if about to rise and continue his work, then sat down again for another cigarette to strengthen himself for an afternoon of charcuterie.

The day had lost its momentum and the pace was much slower after the mid-morning feast. The joints of meat, fat, offal and any other spare parts were all carried into a small room adjoining the house in which stood a scrubbed wooden table with a hand-operated mincer attached. This was where Alexandro would act out the grand finale of the all-day dramatic production. Meat was minced, garlic, pepper and paprika added. The heart, lungs and chunks of solid blood were boiled and minced too. Herbs arrived from the kitchen which were added to the mixtures. The slabs of fat were sprinkled with salt, pepper and garlic and it was explained to me that that was all that would happen to them. It was not even cooked, simply allowed to go cold, and set, and then eaten.

Misu arrived with the steaming pig's head which had been boiling away somewhere else in the house and Alexandro set to work on it with his fingers. "If you need to use a knife, it means it is not properly cooked." Then he pulled out the tongue, skinned it, and piled the whole lot into the mincer. There was a job for everyone; no one escaped a task. Romi was given chunks of skin with a thick slice of fat attached and in a clean cauldron over a flame, he gradually rendered them down till the skin was frying in its own fat – a sort of pork scratching. He stirred so the fat would not burn and Misu occasionally removed a piece and squeezed the fat till he felt precisely the right texture between his fingers, and then enough pieces of fried skin to fill a large pan were spooned out and drained.

Alexandro, working like a machine now, did not pause from his sausage making as he pumped lumps of fat, boiled blood and head-meat into sausage skins adding herbs and pepper as he did so. Romi was forever declaring, "Pork without the wine is like a fish without a bicycle" but with the *tsoica* pumping through his body, he shouted, "The sausage without the garlic is like the woman without the . . ." and he cut himself short as Rodica came round the corner carrying a pan into which a sausage at least ten feet long was to be coiled.

By four in the afternoon, the entire process came to a slithering halt as every part of the pig had been minced, preserved, or eaten. Alexandro had a satisfying cigarette and surveyed the mountains of food he had sculpted from the pink beast that eight hours before was grunting innocently in its sty, blissfully unaware of its fate. Then we were summoned to table and again it groaned under the weight of food. But this time it was sausages, heavy with garlic and paprika, some with lumps of fat as thick as your thumb. There was more sour soup with pork in it, and lumps of fried pork, and pork fat, and more pork, and sausage and . . . and I felt quite sick and only with the help of a pickled cucumber or two to dull the greasiness did I somehow get through the day.

Predictably, the talk turned to politics, Ceausescu, and the revolution. Romi's brother arrived and, always the joker, put his head round the door and asked if the pig was dead. "Yes," Romi cried, "the pig died in '89" and there was a triumphant loud cheer.

And that was Romania and its pigs. I had seen what I came to see; the pig still at the heart of a culture, an everyday companion to townsfolk as well as villagers, a guarantee that they will not go hungry no matter how vile the winter, or the regime. I had seen the killing of the pig as it has been enacted in every part of the world where pigs are kept and the peasant culture flourishes. I had shared the joy of eating the food the sacrificed pig provided, and survived it. And now I was ready for home.

Romi drove me to the airport by back roads through villages and vineyards, down rutted tracks, through the midst of flocks of wandering geese, around the occasional sow and litter that had chosen to bed-down for the day in the middle of the road. It was a pleasant way to leave Romania and with plenty of time before the flight, there seemed to be no hurry.

But as we got closer to Timisoara, the fog came down, visibility was less than a 100 yards and Romi, unused to travelling far from Salonta, got lost. We stopped and asked an old man the way and followed his directions but soon ended up facing a ploughed field with only the muddiest of rutted tracks down one edge. "I saw planes back there," I said, but it was a military airfield, not the airport and only added to the confusion. I now had a desperate urge to be back in the comfort of Vienna. My stomach was aching from having eaten ten pork meals in seven days. I was at that point of desperation where I would have considered armed robbery for a chew of a carrot or apple, or anything with a vitamin in it. As the state of the road worsened, Romi, fearful that the Dacia might take no more punishment, asked a truck driver for directions. They were completely opposite to those given by the old man. "So why did the old man tell me to go that way,?" asked Romi. "Because that *is* the way to the airport, if you are going by horse and cart!" was the reply.

5

o not believe for one minute that everyone who works in the meat industry here in Britain believes in what they produce. Although not all of them will admit it, their senses and sensibilities have been harnessed often against their better judgement, and they have succumbed to the direction of some authority or other which has decreed the sort of meat that we will be able to buy. We have not been given a choice. In fact, choice has been removed from us, for those who want a bit of fat on their bacon can go and whistle for it if it happens to be no longer the taste of the trade. It is not as though they can take their custom elsewhere, for those with the most influence have ensured by ruthless use of economic force that there can never be any competition, and so no choice. If it were politics we would be living in a totalitarian state, but since it is only food and we do not care much for making a fuss, we have let it slide. And so we have got we deserve, and the pig has ended up with what it does *not* deserve, which is an often miserable life, lived in vain to produce an inferior kind of food. What a way to treat a loyal servant of centuries.

So on my travels I did not bother to go to the big factories. I never had to don the white wellingtons or the hair net, for I was never in the mood for smooth-talking platitude, condescension, the stink of profit before all else. Instead, for my final foray, I went back to the north to meet men who knew how a pig should be treated, and who know how to take the care needed to produce the glorious and varied foods only the pig can give us.

I started in an unlikely spot, on the outskirts of Leeds, in a small house on a modern housing estate which, luckily for Trevor Gamble, has a 40 foot garage. It is in the garage that Trevor cures his own sides of bacon, fat pieces of belly, to give him the sort of bacon on his plate without which his weekend would not be complete. It was pitch dark as I drove round a web of newly-built Crescents, Avenues, Closes and Streets, looking for a man who knew what to do with a pig.

Trevor is in his mid-forties but the pig culture was sufficiently alive in recent years for his wife to remember regularly using lard for the chip-pan, stored in a pig's bladder: "Yer just cut it in half and used it when you wanted some more fat."

"My father was a butcher, an old country butcher," Trevor told me. "We used to do a lot of pig killing; it went on till the late sixties, I suppose, goin' out, killin' pigs. But not so much for cottagers in later years, more for farmers. There was one old chap I remember, in Barwick in Elmet, he were. He always used to buy a runt from a litter an' feed it up. He treated it like a pet. Well, we used to go up there and kill it for him and when we had, he used to go in the house and cry his heart out, he was that upset. Well, it used to upset us too because we then had to put his pig on a sort of stretcher and cart it away, then we'd cut it up for him and one pig would nearly last him two years. But we used to go all over, killin' pigs. We'd dress 'em in washhouses, foldyards sometimes. The only mistake I remember making was when I did one on oat straw once, and the pig went yeller. Yeh, I remember that."

I had been introduced to Trevor by a vet, Geraldine Hale, who worked alongside him in an abattoir where he had a job as a meat inspector. She wrote to me, sharing my view about the depths to which our treatment of pig meat had sunk:

"It would be a pity if the sound knowledge of the likes of these men were lost, as it has already been to some modern bacon factories which may take only the best pigs and slaughter them cleanly and humanely but then treat the meat produced in a manner which could almost be described as profane."

In particular, it was Trevor's memories of a particular pub in which I was interested. It was remote, in the Yorkshire Dales, and somehow the accounts I had heard of the Saturday night revels when a pig would be killed and a celebration held, summed up for me the entire culture which had been lost. To a new generation it may seem distasteful to kill a pig and then sit around, partying, enjoying the spoils of the deadly deed; but in the name of some kind of progress we prefer to turn our backs on the idea of killing and as a result we have learnt to discount the lives the animals lead.

The pig that was killed on a Saturday night at the Falcon in Arncliffe could not have wished for a better life, or a more humane end. As it was destined to become the star attraction of a long-planned feast, it would have been fed and cared for as if it were royalty. Its dispatch seems to have been a semi-public affair too and so throughout its life the pig had guarantees of careful husbandry and compassionate killing. We, on the other hand, have allowed our pigs to be reared behind the concealing asbestos walls of farmers' big sheds, and mass-killed in factories which we are too scared to enter for fear of what we might see. Which is a healthier approach?

"There used to be two brothers run this pub, the Falcon. One were a bit slow, not daft, just a bit slow. Always stewed from the night before. They kept Welsh cross pigs and they'd get in touch with us and ask us to come up on a Saturday and do the pig for 'em. Well, we used to get a rope round the pig's nose and then round its back leg and walk it up the village to the wash-house. The idea was that if it tried to get away, you could give a yank on the rope and its back leg would go from under it and it couldn't run far. Trouble with pigs is that there's nothin' to get 'old of. Some o' the lads from the Dales used to say they dreaded pig killing time. They'd say 'it used to take 8 or 9 of us to hold't pig down.' They used to wrestle it off its feet, you see. Well, that's no way to do it. Our way were't best.

"Well, we'd get to the wash-house and they'd say 'would yer like a drink boys?' We'd probably have a rum and coffee. Then there was beer throughout the morning. Then we 'ad a ploughman's lunch. Me and my pal Bruce, I can tell you, were legless by now.

"We allus shot the pigs, with a proper humane killer. We'd bleed the pigs into a bucket and someone had to keep stirring it. That was taken down to their mother's. They always used to shout, 'Get runnin' before it sets.' It was for the black pudding. They always put a bit of mint in it. We used to give the stomachs away – gypsies used to have them and they'd wash them and toast them, you know.

"Well, that evening, all the locals arrived at the pub for a grand 'Blood Pudding Supper' You should have seen what were on those plates. There was the blood pudding itself, the fried bread, an egg or two, bit o' liver. They would all turn up in their best clothes, too. I'll tell you a thing: by the time we came out of the pub, the birds were singin'."

Trevor's wife remembers the post-war days of rationing when pig food was in short supply, and a licence was needed before a pig could be privately killed.

"I can remember my Dad had killed a pig and we didn't have a licence and just as we got it into the kitchen sink, the policeman came knocking on the door. Well, we hauled that pig out of the sink and dragged it upstairs and put it in the bath till the policeman had gone."

Trevor joined in. "There was this chap we knew who had a motorbike and sidecar and he had this side of bacon stuffed in the sidecar. Well, the police followed him down this lane 'cos it looked a bit suspicious and they found him unloading this side of bacon and draggin' it up a ladder into the loft over a barn. The chap gave himself up and handed over the illegally killed side of bacon to the police. 'Why did you do that?' I asked. 'Because,' replied the chap 'if the copper had gone up that ladder he'd 'av seen t'other three sides that were hangin' up there.'" Trevor leaned forward, confidentially, "There was a church in the Dales, you know, where the bacon used to hang in the tower. T'vicar used to cut hi'self a piece off every Sunday."

"I can't eat that supermarket stuff so I still do bit for myself. I've got a box in the garage. Fat bellies are what I like to cure. I just rub the skin with salt, pepper and brown sugar. Pity you weren't here last week else yer could 'av 'ad a bit. Trouble is nobody wants to eat meat at all these days. And pigs don't look like pigs any more. We used to kill all the breeds. Wessex, Essex, Berkshire. Pigs these days may have got lots of muscle, but they've no taste, I'll tell you that."

I bid him farewell and watched him close the door on the innocent semi-detached house where no one would guess Trevor's porky secret, hidden in the garage. It was a long way from Romania where everyone kept a pig, and a big step from the days when the Yorkshire Dales could boast a pig in most back-yards; but it was a start. Trevor Gamble may be showing connoisseurs of real ham and bacon the way forward, and not the way back.

One final heave northwards to pay the last call of my ham-seeking tours. I had saved my best call till last although I was not to know it till I arrived. But there were clues. I read once that Darlington had no less than six pork butchers, and the fact stuck in my mind. I must also confess to a belief that has remained largely unshaken, and that is that the further north you go, the better the chances of finding pork being taken seriously. I arrived in the centre of Darlington on a cold day in mid-January with sleet in the air and a cutting wind from the southeast. I was seeking Zissler & Son, famous pork butchers of this town for over a century and I was given the address as being in Bondgate. I did not have a map so asked at the information counter at the bus station. "What d' yer want in Bondgate?" asked the girl behind the counter. "Zissler's," I said, hesitating in case she had not heard of it.

"Oh!" she cried, "Zissler's!" as if Zissler's needed no address, such was its fame.

It turned out to be a small shop, on a busy road junction, which might be easily missed by a less than careful eye, but my antennae for pork are now such that I had no trouble homing in. The sign above the window was the give-away. For some reason, all the best butchers' shops have their names in embossed gold leaf proudly hung above the window. This was no exception. I crossed the road and as the contents of the window came into focus I knew that this was going to be special. First to hit my eye were the shimmering pork pies, almost as golden as the letters above the shop and competing for brilliance with the freshly-cooked Scotch eggs close by. Everything was sitting on chilly white marble slabs which looked as though they had given a century of service, and had other centuries yet to give. Next to the pies were chunky farmhouse sausages and nestling next to them was black pudding which had not been forced into nouveau black skins, but simply baked in a tray from which thick slices were cut to order. Nothing here looked mucked about with; it was all good, simple, quality food. A tray of cooked pig's trotters filled the left hand side of the window next to a fine pile of breadcakes filled with either ham or pork and lashings of dripping, just like the ones I remembered grandfather buying on his way to work at that pork shop which had long since disappeared.

Through the door, and I was confronted by the smell I remembered and had travelled so far to find. It was not the usual butcher's shop odour of salt, bleach and flesh; but a heady mixture of fresh, hot baking, roasting meat sizzling from the oven and spicy scents from freshly-baked sausage rolls. I could have stood, inhaled, and enjoyed that moment for far longer than it took for Mr Paul Zissler to invite me into his back office where he sat at the roll-top desk and asked to be excused for a moment while he went to the back kitchen to give a pot a stir.

The current Mr Zissler is a youthful, energetic chap who is happy to confess to his German ancestor's vital error of having landed by ship in West Hartlepool in 1869. "He couldn't speak English but knew that he wanted to open a pork shop, which was what he knew about. So he went to Leeds and opened one there. Sadly it was in the Jewish quarter."

I mentioned the shopfront, which apparently dates from 1903, and the embossed gold lettering which marks a pork butcher as distinctively as a red and white striped pole used to mark a barber.

"It's called the Brilliant process, making those letters. The letters are cut out of wood and then coated with gold leaf. Only trouble with them is that they drop off because of the vibration of the buses." I watched the customers carefully, to see who these people were who still had a taste for the good things in life. None of them looked much under 40, except for a few girls buying a pork sandwich. This in itself is significant for I imagine a burger would have been cheaper.

"Most of my customers are of the old school. They've always come to a shop like this. There's no point trying to compete with supermarkets, we just can't match them on price."

As we spoke, a delivery of meat arrived. Not whole pigs, but parts of a carcass which might be made into several joints. "Pigs these days are far too lean. Look at this one, a supermarket buyer would not go anywhere near it, but I'd send a pig back if it was too lean. What I like to see is half to three quarters of an inch of fat on its back. This one has got two layers, see." True, there was a decent layer of fat over the meat, then a distinct vein and more fat. "One is its winter coat, and the other is its natural fat. Never get past a supermarket buyer, but it's lovely pork. I like a firm feel to the fat and you only get that from breeding and feeding. Female pigs as well, they're the best. There's too much muscle tension in boar pork."

Looking around the shop, past the deep tray of dripping with the rich, brown jellied gravy nestling in the bottom, past the bright red brawns coloured with dye (a local preference nobody can explain), there seemed to be little missing. Every part of the pig was here, except the offals. Livers and kidneys, yes; but where were the chitterlings?

"Ah, chitterlings," said Zissler, "do you know, we used to sell hundredweights of chitterlings every week, but nothing now. Same with tripe. I believe there's only one tripe factory left, they've all closed. It goes for dog food."

But apart from the chitterlings, which are the pig's intestines, every other part of the pig seemed to be on sale here. Zissler makes his own brawns, and savoury ducks, or faggots. "We used to do our own polony but the market for that has dropped right off. It's those dried, wizened spicy sticks in packets they sell in supermarkets that's done it. But January is a quiet time and I'll start making polony once again when we get to Easter. But all these things; polony, savoury ducks, black pudding, they were all designed to get rid of the bits of pork you couldn't sell as joints. Very clever really."

We left the office and went through to the back kitchen where two ladies stamp out pork pies, roll sausage rolls, fry Scotch eggs. Machines for stamping the lids onto the pies looked old enough to have been a relic from grandfather Zissler's day, with warming flames bursting from the press to prevent the pastry sticking. Pig's trotters were gently simmering in one large pot, ham stock in another for filling the pork pies, roasted pigs' cheeks came out of the oven to be taken straight into the shop when cool.

The twin doors of the oven opened and from the steaming mouth came freshly baked pork pies, golden on top, just a few of the 2000 pies Zissler's sell each week. In a corner, the deft hand of Esther was rolling pastry round a long sausage of meat that would eventually be cut into sausage rolls. We supped hot tea, tasted cooked sausages, I was given a pound of the pork and tomato flavour, and I bought an extra-large pork pie still warm from the oven which Zissler filled with hot ham stock fresh from the pan. If I carried this carefully, it would eventually set into the finest jelly within the pie.

Then, alas, we came to hams. I had by now travelled over a thousand miles in Britain and across to eastern Europe in search of an ultimate ham which would match up to my unfulfilled childhood expectations. With no small amount of sorrow on his face, Paul Zissler admitted that his hams were *Danish*. "The trouble is," he explained, "my customers buy on price and consistency. They want it to taste the same every time, and they want it cheap. I have tried the English hams but I simply can't get what I want at a price I can expect my customers to pay." Fair enough. But he had broken my heart.

And that sums up exactly what has happened to the pig and foods it gives us. We eat with relish, if the price is right. So let us not complain that what we are offered these days is poor stuff since we are not prepared to pay extra for better. Let us not criticise farmers for their intensive methods, as long as we are unwilling to pay any extra for meat produced from more humane systems. The fact has to be faced that the demeaning way in which we have come to treat the pig and its products is a direct result of too much food being available too cheaply. The cheaper it is made – by whatever awful means – the cheaper we expect to get it. It is a truism in the retailing industry that the customer is always right, but in the case of the Whole Hog, the customer has never been more wrong.

But this does not mean that the search is over, or that none of the hams I tasted was anything other than first-rate; for Zissler's Danish ham was of the finest, and so were all the others hams and bacons tasted.

But there is one sure, ultimate step to take to be certain of the ultimate ham. You must keep a pig of your own.

Part Two

Pigs are very beautiful animals. Those who think otherwise are those who do not look at anything with their own eyes, but only through other people's eyeglasses. The actual lines of a pig (I mean of a really fat pig) are among the loveliest and most luxuriant in nature; the pig has the same great curves, swift and yet heavy, which we see in rushing water or in rolling clouds...He has that fuller, subtler and more universal kind of shapeliness which the unthinking (gazing at pigs and distinguished journalists) mistake for a mere absence of shape. For fatness itself is a valuable quality. While it creates admiration in the onlookers, it creates modesty in the possessor. If there is anything on which I differ from the monastic institutions of the past, it is that they sometimes sought to achieve humility by means of emaciation. It may be that the thin monks were holy, but I am sure it was the fat monks who were humble. Falstaff said that to be fat is not to be hated, but it certainly is to be laughed at, and that is a more wholesome experience for the soul of man.

From *The Uses of Diversity*, by G.K. Chesterton

Unless you keep your own pig and cure your own hams, you are never fully going to recapture what we have lost. Retracing steps is usually harder than forging blindly ahead, and it is true with pigs. You may be lucky; it is just possible that you have a friend of a like mind who keeps a pig, or knows someone who does, who will cure and smoke the meat as you would wish it. But these are a long string of coincidences and, quite frankly, if you are able, you are better off keeping your own.

If someone should try to dampen your enthusiasm by insisting that pigs are mucky and smelly, I think you should admit to yourself (but never to *them*) that this is true. Much is always being written about pigs being the cleanest of animals, and they are in the sense that they are clean in their personal habits, preferring to dung in a regular place. But dung they do, and it smells. Mind you, it is no worse than the regular inhalation of diesel or petrol exhaust fumes, and if you want to look on the bright side, you will have a garden that will never want for fertiliser again. But you have to admit straight away that on hot days you will be able to cut the air with a knife, and flies will never be far away. If this does not put you off, all you have to remember is to have your pigs some way from the house, be extra careful about cleanliness in the heat of the summer, and that's it.

Housing, feeding and fattening the pig we shall discuss, but we need to consider your relationship with your pig, which you should have firm views upon, before you take so much as a step in the direction of a breeder with a view to buying an animal.

It must not be a pet. If you start giving it a name when it is a couple of months old, you will not be able to kill it in five months' time. In the days when cottagers kept pigs, the burden of necessity weighed heavily on their shoulders and they had no alternative but to slaughter the hog that had lived so close to them that it was at the stage when it was welcome around the fireplace. But in the less needy age in which we live you will come up with a thousand reason not to slaughter Polly, Spot, or Grunt. And you will end up with an overgrown, over-fat hog which is going to have to be slaughtered one day, but will be of little eating value when it is. You will then decide that pig-keeping was a foolish experiment on which to embark and the supermarket bacon counter will be your next port of call. You will blame the pig, but it will be your fault.

There is a way round this, providing you have the room – and my guess would be that unless you have somewhere between a quarter or half an acre of land you might be well advised not to consider pig-keeping at all, for pigs love to roam and they should be given that opportunity. Buy yourself an "in-pig gilt". A gilt is a female pig that has yet to produce a litter; in-pig speaks for itself. You will then have a pig which you can name, send Christmas cards to, tuck up last thing at night, have children tickle the belly of, and all the other things that are enjoyably done to pigs. When she arrives, she might be a year old and still have a couple of months to go before farrowing. This gives you plenty of time to get used to her ways, and she to yours; and as her pregnancy progresses she will become more placid and you will get to know her even better. She will never see the brine tub; she will become part of the family and live many long and happy years.

Her litter (of probably 10 or 11) will be your first crop. They will be adorable. You will fatten them slowly for six months, and as they achieve a size, they will go to the butcher. By then they will be rowdy, misbehaving teenagers and you will be glad to see the back of them. There will have been so many of them that you will not know them individually; and no hearts will be broken when they leave. When your friends and neighbours taste the wonders of what you have produced, I doubt you will have any trouble selling the meat; and depending on how fast you can either consume or sell it, you can decide on when your pet sow will next be sent to a boar.

While we are at this stage in the planning process, the subject of slaughter is worth discussing; for to have a dozen hefty hogs ready for the kill and nowhere to send them is dispiriting. I mention this because all the mistakes that can be made in small-scale pig-keeping, I have made. So ask around, find out who keeps pigs in the way in which you intend to keep yours. Ring up the abattoirs in the *Yellow Pages*, ask if they will accept a "private kill". It is as important to be as kind to a pig when it has to be dispatched as it was when it was grunt-ing in the sty. Pigs which have to undertake lengthy journeys to be slaughtered, along with thousands of others, when the furthest they have ever travelled in their lives is the length of your garden with their brothers and sisters, are not being kindly treated in my opinion. There was a time when a village butcher would kill a pig for you, but they and our small slaughterhouses are now on the endangered species list and you may well find that killing your pigs represents a major hurdle in your plans. But if you cannot promise your pig a decent end to its life, you should not even give it a beginning.

All that having been said, and a few basic points having been mulled over, the choice of breed of pig is crucial. There is no doubt that any form of highly-bred, improved and genetically mucked-about-pig, is to be avoided. The pigs that are reared intensively, even the ones that live out of doors, are products of a process which has engineered them and finely tuned them to the needs of the modern, efficient and profit-conscious farmer. That is their business. There are no parallels whatsoever between what we are trying to do and the commercial farmer's objectives, and it is no use pretending that in some way we know better than he does. We are not playing the same game and so our rules do not apply to him, and vice-versa. In his collection of essays under the title *Field and Farm* , the rural writer Richard Jefferies warns us,

". . . it is curious that almost all townsmen who have no practical experience of farming, but who take a deep interest in it, and think no life so desirable, are warm advocates of the pig, and do not scruple to denounce agriculturalists as little better than fools for not utilising this animal as they might. The farmer who hears this of course very naturally shrugs his shoulders, and recommends them to try it themselves."

Just because we choose to ignore the rules of modern farming and the tastes that have been inflicted upon us by a subtly domineering food industry does not mean that we are in any way returning to an inferior product. There is no doubt that a great deal of pork and bacon was pretty dire stuff. Jefferies goes on:

"All of us who possess any reminiscences of farming can recollect when to kill a pig of immense size was a time of rejoicing. Fat three fingers thick was rather a recommendation. Rusty bacon was assumed to be the natural food of the labourer. . . (but) . . . the townsman who comes down to breakfast in the morning, and expects to find a tempting rasher ready for him, would turn away disgusted from the greasy, coarse, strong-flavoured bacon which the farmer formerly fatted and cured."

There is clearly some balance to be struck here and our objective must be to resurrect the qualities that we desire, without imposing upon ourselves the undoubted deficiencies of the peasant's system of pig-keeping. It is not difficult.

Choose carefully the breed of pig you wish to keep. A century or more ago you would have been spoilt for choice for almost every part of the country, if not every county, took pride in its own breed of hog. The book *British Husbandry* of 1837 which was ". . . published under the superintendence of the Society for the Diffusion of Useful Knowledge . . ." proclaims in the introduction to its chapter "On Swine":

"Pork, both in its fresh and salted state, is an article of such universal consumption, and the hog is such a profitable consumer of every eatable species of offal, that pigs are not only reared by every farmer, but by every cottager who can find means to feed them; for there is no animal which yields so great a quantity of flesh in return for the kind of food which it consumes, and it has been not unjustly called the 'poor man's stock'."

Interestingly, the book then goes on to list four basic breeds of pig; the Berkshire, the Chinese, the Highland and the Irish. The Berkshire, of course, survives today, but of the other three species we can only speculate. Of the Irish species it says, "though living in the same hut as sumptuously as his master, is an ill-formed animal, scarcely meriting notice." The Highland pig does no better; " ..an ugly brindled monster, the very epitome of the wild boar, yet scarcely bigger than an English terrier:

"His bristled back a trench impaled appears,
And stands erected like a field of spears."
(Dr Hibbert's *Account of the Shetland Islands*)

It is the Chinese pigs who seem to rate the most highly and it seems to be from these that many of our native breeds of pig are descended.

"There are two distinct species – the white and the black; the former better shaped than the latter, but less hardy and prolific. Both are, however, small-limbed, ears and head fine, round in the carcass, thin-skinned and a head so embedded in the neck, that when quite fat, the end only of the snout can be seen."

The Complete Grazier of 1877 lists a further extraordinary breed known as the Cheshire which grew to vast sizes and weights. An

94

account is given of one particular pig; "It measured, from the nose to the end of the tail, 3 yards and 8 inches, and was in height 4 feet 5½ inches. It weighed when alive, 12 cwt 2 qrs 10lbs."

Clearly, the pigs we have now are descended from ingenious and painstaking crosses of any, or all, of these pigs and although the Berkshires, Tamworths, Large Blacks, Middle Whites and Saddlebacks survive today, there are many that have fallen by the wayside, as indeed might any of the pigs which are now protected under a rare breeds umbrella. British Husbandry, for example, goes on to list the Essex Half Blacks, the Shropshire, the Woburn, Dishleys, and even the Tonquin. This is no place to try and unravel the family tree of our currently surviving pig breeds, other than to remember that all pigs outside the mainstream of intensive farming are vulnerable to extinction since they rely for their survival on the enthusiasm of their owners, and not the profits they can produce.

So, you have little choice when it comes to choosing the sort of pig you wish to keep, and the decision is quite easy. Buy a pig which you will be happy to look in the eye first thing in the morning, last thing at night, and at all times in between. Never was it more true than in the keeping of pigs that beauty lies in the eye of the beholder. I happen to fancy the Large Black; a noble breed which produces pigs which are good grazers, considerate mothers, and good company too. Their ears are long and floppy and they will reach a certain age where they rely less on their eyes for navigation, increasingly depending on their noses. But equally, I can see how you might fall in love with a swarthy Berkshire, a finely marked Saddleback, a gingery Tamworth, a pinky Middle White or a dear Gloucester Old Spot. Within the confines of your ambitions, which are to please yourself in the matter of hams and bacon, all these old and endangered breeds of pigs will do. They are sensible animals from a more sensible age, and over the years they have lost none of the instincts for survival which enable them to thrive on far less feeding than their highly bred contemporaries. True, they will take longer to fatten and the fat will be thicker, but if these matters are of concern to you, you will not have got this far in this book. Have a look at some pictures, pick yourself a pig, and go for it. The Rare Breeds Survival Trust will point you in the direction of breeders and the only word of advice I would give – falling in love with your sow is something that only you can engineer – is to see that there are appropriate boars in your area kept by owners who are willing to have others use them. Artificial insemination of pigs is a messy job and for professionals. If there is no suitor for your sow you are never going to produce any piglets. Of course, you can cross your sow with any old male pig; but if you are keeping a rare and special breed then it seems worth putting some effort into perpetuating it. I have on occasions, due to 'ack of local Black boar, crossed our Large Black sows with a commercial white pig. Neither side seemed to mind; but when it came to putting pork on plate, the flavour, texture, and juiciness of the meat was so far removed from what we had been used to that we vowed never to call upon the services of Cyril again. Cyril, the Large White boar, was a friendly chap who was fortunate enough to live in the middle of Ipswich next to a bakery. At the end of the day, it was Cyril's good fortune to feast on all manner of doughnuts, vanilla slices and fondant fancies. But none of his sweetness ever found its way through to his offspring.

To give you a grounding in pig husbandry, I have consulted my regular sources. None of them is modern, some date from the nineteenth century, and hardly anywhere does the word profit appear. Nevertheless their advice is sound. In particular, I recommend *The Pioneering Pig* by Norman Blake published in the 1950s. It is an anarchic little book by a man who sensed that farming was not going the pig's way and sought to reassure his readers that a traditional approach still had much to offer. This book may still be found in second-hand bookshops. But let us take as our creed in the matter of keeping pigs some words written by the distinguished oral historian, George Ewart Evans, who faithfully recorded the words of east Suffolk farm workers and villagers who were the dying remnants of a former way of rural life. In 1956 he wrote:

"Another instance of the wisdom of old traditional practices is shown by the rearing of pigs. It has recently been found that young pigs often do much better in the low, stuffy and apparently unhealthy pigsties of cottagers and smallholders who keep pigs as a sideline than in the roomy, specially constructed modern piggeries...the rough pigsty with its low roof and poor ventilation was much nearer the ideal for the young pig, as in the wild state it would spend its first weeks in a warm *nest* that its mother had made for it in dense well-protected undergrowth."

So let us assume, as he does, that the old way is the best, and pursue it with vigour.

Your pig will need some shelter in which to escape the winter winds and rains as much as the scorching rays of summer sunshine. You can easily buy a corrugated arc, which is no more than a curved sheet of corrugated tin, boarded at each end. I have used these, and they are fine. They are not appealing on the eye, but they are easily moved, easily repaired, and quite cheap. Be sure to buy a strong one; an extra fifty quid spent now will be money well spent for a sow will take every opportunity to rub herself against it if nothing else is available, and the full force of a sow's bodily contortions can inflict serious and lasting damage on a flimsy structure.

But the best housing for a pig must be the cottager's sty. It consists of two parts; a low, fronted house in which the pig rests and sleeps, and an outer run where she comes to feed and exercise. Dimensions are hard to lay down but the run should be at least three yards square or she is going to be rather cramped. The shelter need be no more than eight feet square. We are fortunate in that we have a fine little row of sties and it is interesting to note that when these were built, which we believe to be around 1882, more attention was given to the detail of the construction than in any of the other farm buildings, even the stable. That is why the roofs are neatly tiled, and even felted to provide extra insulation. They are carefully sited too, with their backs to the cold east winds, and the runs facing south so the pigs can bask in the sun.

In an ideal world, your pig will have two residences: summer quarters and a winter retreat. If you are able to confine a pig in an orchard, or copse, or other overgrown and tangly little corner for the summer (electric fencing will do the job) then all you need provide is the simplest of shelters made from materials to hand. When the autumn rains make the ground so boggy that all the soft soil lifted by a summer's effort on the part of your pig's snout turns to sticky mud, you can then bring her back to the cosy confines of the sty. In the enclosed part of the sty is where your pig will probably farrow, although on one famous occasion, Alice, our Large Black sow, decided to have her litter half-way, maintaining her own comfort by wedging her body in the doorway with her snout in the warm interior, while at the same time effortlessly expelling new-born piglets into the frosty air on the other side of the doorway. The problem was that the piglets could not climb back indoors, so we had to shift them.

Pigs are generally good mothers; but big, fat, ungainly sows have a habit of rolling on piglets, and killing them. It is not deliberate, as far as I know, but a hefty pig in a hazy and exhausted post-farrowing state flings its body-mass around in a fairly uncontrolled way and it is a miracle that more piglets do not succumb to their mother's steam roller tendencies. In *Stephens' Book of the Farm* (1884) that great Scottish agriculturalist advises:

"It is a great advantage to have stout battens fixed along the sides of that part of the sty on which the bedding is laid. The battens require to be 1 ½ to 1 ¾ inch thick, and from 4 to 6 inches broad, depending somewhat on the strength and nature of the wood. They should be firmly fixed with their under surface from 8 to 9 inches above the level of the floor, and should be at least 4 inches distant from the floor. Galvanised iron tubing 2 ½ inches in diameter may be used instead of the battens, and is considered better from a sanitary point of view, but the iron is cold. The wood is much more comfortable for the pigs. This arrangement is a useful protection to the young pigs, as they can creep in between the mother and the wall and obtain a share of the maternal warmth without running the risk of being overlaid."

This idea is a simple one. The wooden rail, set about 18 inches from the wall, effectively provides a total exclusion zone, a solid barrier behind which the piglets can lie without any fear of mother coming and resting her great bulk upon them.

You will note that although he nods briefly in the direction of hygiene, and not at all at the notion of cost, paramount in his concerns is the comfort of the pigs. However, I took his advice when I renovated the first of our sties and duly built the rail, exactly as he prescribes. In order to persuade the young piglets to make use of the safe haven it provided, I hung an infra-red lamp above it, hoping it would draw the piglets towards the warmth. On checking the litter last thing at night, I found the sow, firmly wedged between wall and rail and enjoying the heat of the lamp like an old lady soaking up the Bournemouth sun, and the litter of eleven, shivering in the cold, running around to try and stay warm.

If you wish to build yourself a cottager's sty, the best thing is to find one and copy it. But as they are scarce, I offer a few nuggets of advice from a useful little booklet published by the National Federation of Young Farmers Clubs, at a guess, in the early fifties. It offers all manner of alternative pig housings ranging from the converted back end of an old lorry, to the romantically irresistible hut made from felled timbers, straw and bracken. But on the subject of the cottager's sty it offers:

"WALLS: In building the walls remember that pigs have a hearty appetite for wood, and unless we are careful we may find one morning that they have eaten their way out of the pen overnight and are frolicking about in the garden. Wooden walls must therefore be lined with metal. Old enamel advertising signs or corrugated iron are suitable. We must be careful not to leave any projecting corners or edges on which the pigs can bite, nor must there be any chance of a pig getting his snout under a projection, for his lifting powers are amazing."

Never underestimate the power of the snout. We have old feeding rings made of cast iron and large enough to feed a litter of a dozen. They are too heavy to be carried by one man alone and so if we have to move them unaided, we roll them. I have seen a sow, however, take command of one of these heavy rings by placing her snout under the rim and flicking it in the air as easily as if it were a child's frisbee. Let this serve as a reminder that the rarer breeds of pigs are rarely vicious or bad-tempered, but if they were minded to be nasty, they have the potential to do much damage.

Before leaving the business of housing your pig, it is well worth remembering the usefulness of straw. I have, in the past, housed young pigs in a shelter made of no more than bales of straw; but it is essential to provide some framework in which the bales can sit otherwise a bit of a shove from an agitated pig's rump and the entire house will come tumbling down.

As a blueprint, I offer an extract from *The Homesteader's Handbook*, an anthology of traditional American farming advice which often works as well on this side of the Atlantic:

"It would pay every farmer to put up in the pastures some kind of protection for his sheep, hogs and cattle. Where labour is scarce and hay and straw are plentiful and cheap, a condition which prevails in many large sections, straw sheds and barns are very profitable. Put up a framework of posts 8 feet high, 16 feet wide, and as long as needed. [I would suggest much smaller for pigs alone.] The posts are hewed evenly on two sides and set so that a bale of straw will fit snugly between them. They are cut off at a uniform height and a 2 by 6 spiked securely on top. Rafters are nailed to this and covered loosely with poles. Baled straw is used for the sides. After the sides are up the roof is covered 2 feet deep with loose straw held in place with a few poles that are tied together in pairs and placed over the ridge. Several of these sheds have stood for five years and have not needed any attention."

Do not imagine for one minute that your pigs are being in any way subjected to second-class accommodation simply because they are not surrounded by plastered building blocks and do not have the luxury of a corrugated tin roof over their heads. Straw is good stuff for sheltering animals, and on nights when the frost comes down most pigs, given the choice, would keep themselves snug under thatch. It breathes too.

As far as furniture goes, your pig will need some kind of trough. Traditional pig-feeding rings are hard to come by and tend to be snapped up at auctions by people hell bent on using them to hold dreary plants in their garden. Troughs used for sheep will not do for your pig will be sure to bounce them in the air several times during a feeding frenzy and wooden ones will either break or be chewed to bits. Metal ones will sound for miles around like the bells of hell being rung. The Young Farmers' Club booklet on pig keeping has a good suggestion:

"Make a strong wooden box about 2 feet long 1 foot wide, and 9 inches deep. Line the box with newspaper, and in the bottom put a layer of concrete about 2 inches thick. When this has almost set, lay an empty oil drum, wrapped in newspaper, on its side in the box. Now pour more concrete round the sides of the drum until the level is just below the widest part. When the cement has set, the box may be knocked off and the oil drum removed. If you are successful you will now have a very heavy concrete trough with a smooth inside surface that can easily be kept clean. It will also be the shape a pig cannot overturn, unlike many troughs that are sold."

We must now turn to the important matter of feeding. It is of vital importance to the pig, for obvious reasons, and vital to you from both the points of view of your palate and your pocket. I have to admit that I am far from an expert, and you would be well advised to find one and take their advice, given one or two provisos which I shall mention.

If you are feeding an old-fashioned breed of pig, it needs an old-fashioned diet. I have fed Large Black pigs on barley meal (finely ground barley) and middlings, or sharps as they are known in various parts of the country. Middlings are a by-product of milling and roughly speaking are what is extracted from milled wheat halfway between the bran and the flour. It is generally reckoned to be fine feed for pigs and ours have done well on it. With an older breed of pig, it seems risky to me to ask it to grow too quickly, for it will simply put on huge layers of fat at the expense of meat. Meat seems to need time to grow and so you must give your pig time. A local farmer who kept a herd of commercial pigs and was persuaded by his family to fatten a Tamworth sow for their own consumption, fed it simply on the same high growth, high protein ration that he gave his commercial farm pigs. The sow surely did grow but when it arrived at the butcher's and the carcass was split, the eye of the meat in the chop was the size of a ten pence piece and the fat was sufficiently thick to see an entire family of Russian peasants through a Siberian winter. So a mixture of barley meal to sharps in the ration two to one seems to work; but some would say that there is too little protein in this mixture and I would not argue. I sometimes find that litters get to a certain size and grow no larger and this may well be a protein deficiency. Not that the pig minds; it enjoys its barley and midds. But piglets that stop growing are a pest, for they develop adolescent instincts which would already have been suppressed by the butcher's knife had they continued to grow. So if you want more protein, you can add – if you must – soya or fish meal. In addition, I give a little mineral mixture in each feed which is derived from ground, calcified seaweed molasses to give it sweetness. But if the pigs are free-range and able to root or graze, this never seems to be needed.

It gets more complicated the further you delve into it, and whole books have been devoted to the feeding of swine. The things to avoid are simply turning up at a feed merchant and being given the first bag of pig grub that comes to hand. The labels of these products, designed to meet the needs of the intensive pig rearer, will turn you pale. They contain growth promoters, antibiotics and all manner of additives which have no place in what might be called back-yard pig keeping. Either mix your own if you are confident of the recipe, or go to the supplier whom I have listed in the appendix, and she will help you.

One other word of warning. It is tempting to use a pig as a rubbish bin, and over they years they have proved themselves most efficient converters of kitchen waste into fine food. But modern processed foods are too complicated a chemical cocktail to be innocently hurled at a pig. You would not dream of throwing a lump of left-over meat at a pig (it is illegal anyway unless cooked to a very high temperature outside the scope of the amateur) but you might give it some left-over ice cream, which might contain animal fats. Cabbage leaves, egg-shells, cooked potatoes, milk and cream are safe, but think carefully about all other things.

A few final thoughts from an excellent little booklet called *Garden and Allotment Pig Keeping* by Walter Brett and published in 1941 when the Second World War meant pigs had to live on what they could be given and not what was always most desirable. In his introduction he says:

"The pig, the government says, is the most valuable of all domestic animals – the only part of him that cannot be used in war is his grunt! Pigs not only provide indispensable meat for us to eat but the vital fats needed in the making of munitions. We cannot now import pigs in the quantity required. The farmers cannot make good the shortage. So the cottager must come to the rescue. Cottagers produced 5,000,000 extra pounds of pig meat a year in the last war. They are asked to do the same again, and more, this war."

I think a war-time approach to pig-keeping is not a bad one. It clearly defines the position of the pig as part of the household, and makes every economy in feeding that can be reconciled with a decent end-product. Walter Brett gives certain warnings and encouragements which I will briefly list for I suspect few modern books on pig feeding would bother to mention them.

Vegetable Waste you Shouldn't Use: the tops of potato plants. Also exclude potato peelings. The haulm of runner beans has been known to cause poisoning among pigs, so exclude these, too.

Acorns are Useful: It is better for a garden pig-keeper to dry them in an oven before use. By drying, the flavour is greatly improved, part of the bitter element is evaporated and the whole acorn is rendered more digestible. The feeding value of acorns should be taken as twice that of oats. Do not give acorn meal to pregnant or suckling sows.

Beech-Mast: When large quantities are gathered, it is perhaps best to extract part of the oil by grinding and compression, afterwards steeping the kernels in hot water and pressing for a second time. You can then dry the residue and either break it up to be fed like cake, or grind it into meal.

Pigs in Orchards: If there is a fear that the pig will damage the trees by gnawing the bark, this can be prevented by applying to the trunks of trees a preparation made by stirring a pint potful of clay and one of cow-dung into a bucketful of limewash, with a wineglass of spirits of tar added.

Grass Sods and a Cinder Heap: An aid to contentment for the stay-at-home pig is the practice of putting into the pen a shovelful of grass sods and a heap of cinders or even coal dust. The rootling gives pleasure to the pig and it may be that the cinders clean its mouth and teeth.

I might add to this wise man's words by saying how valuable I have found this last piece of advice. Many is the sickly sow, usually brought low by vigorous milking by a strong and growing litter, that has been rejuvenated by simply throwing a square foot of the lawn into her sty.

The list of things to do and consider may seem bewildering if you have never kept pigs before. But do not be daunted. Give them food, water and shelter and the pigs will look after themselves. They are hardy animals, not easy to break, and it will not be long before they are teaching you their needs. All you will have to do is look and listen.

Poets and pigs are not appreciated until they are dead
Italian Proverb

Y ou are still hesitant about keeping a pig of your own, aren't you? I bet I know why. Is it because you will enjoy the fattening of the pig, but you will not be so happy when it comes to the killing? Very understandable. Although I have been happy to send pigs to slaughter, comforted by the knowledge that I have given them a decent and satisfying life, nevertheless I doubt I would have the courage to pick up the knife and stick the pig myself. It is all too easy for the inexperienced to make a mistake and bring a pig's life to its end in a less than glorious way. I have met a family who reared a pig, and bravely stuck it, and made such a mess of the job that within the half hour they were well on their way to becoming vegans. The knife must plunge swiftly, unhesitatingly, and with surgical precision if it is to perform its task as humanely as possible. Do not do it. Instead, find a licensed slaughterman who might be willing to come and do it for you, for it is still legal to kill a pig in your own back yard for your own use. Most people will send to the nearest and smallest abattoir they can find, as I do, and get their pig back ready jointed.

But to get a flavour of the cottager's back yard when a pig was killed – and the ritual is almost as much a part of the process as the actual sticking – it is worth enjoying some accounts of pig killings, mostly written last century. It was a time of celebration, but Martin Morrissey, who grew up in west Clare in Ireland during the Second World War, remembers in his book *Land of my Cradle Days* his mixed feelings when the winter came and the pig had to be killed:

> At the creamery – the great rural forum of the forties and fifties – a pig killing would be discussed on the following morning among the groups of farmers while they awaited the arrival of the manager in his pony and trap from Cree. As well as being an economic necessity, going to the creamery was a daily social occasion at which the local "characters" amused their fellow suppliers with anecdotes and amusing comments on recent happenings. The news of the killing of a thin pig was a challenge the "characters" couldn't resist as they tried to outdo each other in humorous comments about the unfortunate pig. Somebody would start the ball rolling by saying that he heard the late lamented pig was "a little bit on the thin

side". The comments would come fast and furious – "Wisha God help us, he was like a rasher with a pig's head at one end", or "That bacon will move fast, sure he was a greyhound of a pig to start with . . ."

With my awesome knowledge of the exact day Paddy the butcher was due to arrive, I felt I could not look the creature in the eye in case I would blurt out the dreadful information. His beady, glaring eyes seemed to bore directly into my childish soul. I found other places to play. The further I got from the pig, the less were my feelings of guilt . . . Suddenly I returned to reality (having woken on the morning the pig was due to be killed) with the realisation that the big day had arrived, the day on which my arch enemy, that grumpy pig, the bane of my life, would get his come-uppance. I charged into the kitchen, full of boyish energy, and announced to Dad that I was going to help him kill that pig. He chided me quietly for my blood-thirstiness, sat me on his knee and reminded me that I liked animals and that an animal should never be killed except for necessity. He often said things like that to me though at the time I had no idea what they meant except that they appeared to be sobering thoughts, a damper on my enthusiasm.

I felt myself drawn to walk by the pig-pen to have a quick look, and, perhaps, to gloat over my old enemy. He seemed quite unmoved by all the excitement. He still glared malevolently at me and gave me a warning grunt. However, as the morning wore on, his time became shorter and shorter and I became a little unsure of myself. Enthusiasm was waning rapidly. When I heard Dad say to my mother that it was time to move the big kitchen table out to the car-house, things were becoming very ominous. The more I thought about this matter, the more the pig's personality improved. Maybe he wasn't as bad as I made him out to be; maybe I should have tried harder to make friends with him; maybe he couldn't help being cranky and bad-tempered; maybe he had a bad tooth or a belly-ache and wasn't able to tell us; maybe Dad was killing him because I was always saying that I was afraid of him and that I disliked him so much. By the time Paddy the Butcher arrived on his bicycle and was having a cup of tea, I really liked that pig, while at the same time my liking for the friendly Paddy was on a definite downturn. Why did he have to keep his promise and be so punctual? If only he had got a puncture or even broken the chain of his bicycle on his way to our house, maybe Dad would have changed his mind and there would be no need to kill my friend the pig!

The conversation around the table continued for a while, the great events of the day – compulsory tillage, the war, the scarcity of goods. I was lulled into a false sense of security, my misgivings forgotten, until my father announced that "We may as well make a start, in the name of God." The reins from the horse's winkers were picked up from outside the door. They would be placed on the pig's leg to walk him up the road to the car-house. At this point, my courage failed me and I ran, crying, up the road to our neighbour Eileen, who was like a grown-up sister to me. Not being able to see and hear was, at least, a small consolation. My unmanly tears were a temporary embarrassment, but she understood and didn't make fun of me. Some time later, after peering out the small gate in front of her house, she told me it was safe to go home if I wanted to. I trotted home rather sheepishly, but nobody seemed to have noticed my hour of weakness.

More robust is Harold Cramp's memory of pig-killing days. As one of a family of nine, he helped run the family farm in a Leicestershire village around the time of the First World War:

The pig-sticking was a piece of primordial ceremonial. We really meant no harm to the pig. It was just that it happened to be the central figure in the drama. Much care had been lavished on him, to bring him up to sixteen or eighteen score pounds and now, we thought, he should be almost as proud as we were, that such pleasure for us should ensue from the final act. The killing was done by a butcher from Kibworth, two miles distant. He arrived soon after breakfast in a pony-drawn float and was greeted with the formality due to one of his special skill, and regaled with beer, bread and cheese. Then from his float came the mysterious items of his near priestly craft: a cratch, a thin rope, a bucket with a lid, bristle scrapers and a jute bag with an assortment of knives. The cratch, a sort of sacrificial altar it seemed to me, was a low, wooden, four-legged, stretcher-like affair with handles at each corner. The pig, which had been fasted throughout the previous day, was in no mood to co-operate with those who had brought him no food. Protesting loudly, he was pulled by ears and tail to the cratch in the barn. I always thought it unfortunate for the pig world that they were so badly endowed with means by which man could handle them: no long hair to grasp, no horns to provide leverage, and a body so contoured that it is well nigh impossible to gain a grip on it with hand or rope. Hence the ignominy of the pig's last minutes.

In one swift and easy thrust the butcher slit the pig's throat and the blood gushed into the bucket in rhythmic squirts. The squealing rapidly grew raucous and feeble; soon the pig was pronounced dead and the bleeding complete.

It becomes clear that the custom was usually for an expert to be called in to kill the pig, usually a butcher who arrived with some ceremony. Barrie J Kaye, writing in the *Dalesman* magazine in 1953, remembers a great social occasion in his Yorkshire village:

Often in these days of our limited and unstable meat ration, I recall pig killing day in the Yorkshire village where I spent my youth. That day was one of the few days when we did not have to provide our own entertainment, for that day always closed with a social evening and a supper. Early on the great day grandfather would be lighting the copper fire so that the water would be boiling before Neb the pig-sticker arrived. The arrival of Neb was in itself a rare spectacle for he always arrived in a gaily-painted trap pulled by two milk-white horses. The trap's decorations included paintings of various breeds of pigs done by the skilled hand of a country craftsman famed for his skill in sign-writing. After the customary greetings Neb would enter the house to partake of a glass of my mother's famed gooseberry wine, whilst he exchanged local news and pondered upon childhood reminiscences with my parents. Eventually we persuaded the elders to leave their talking and proceed with the business in hand.

Our cottage pig was no lean weakling but a pig in the region of forty stone. It had to supply a large proportion of our meals for the coming twelve months. Neb had soon arranged himself in his professional clothing and armed himself with several knives of various shapes and sizes. He had now to perform the difficult task of sticking the pig, for he had no humane killer with which first to stun the animal. The pig was first persuaded to stand in the region of several large sacks of straw placed to break its fall, this preventing any bruising. Then the knife fell hard and true, and the red deluge of blood passed into the waiting bucket, it being required for the making of black pudding – a succulent and enjoyable dish.

The pig was then rolled into a bath of boiling water and the scraping began. This consisted of removing the long coarse bristles by using the sharp bases of the kitchen candlesticks. Eventually the pig was hauled and hung on a beam, thus allowing the usual butchering arrangements to take place. After it had hung for several days, depending upon the weather, the secretive and complex matter of salting took place, and even to this day I do not know what ingredients were used, although I think that vinegar, pepper and black treacle, together with a dash of rum, were placed in the long wooden troughs where the hams and the sides were placed during the salting process.

But the most enjoyable time always occurred that evening of the party. What food we devoured – pork pies, sausage rolls, faggot cakes, sparry pie, scraps, fried pork cakes and many others, served with potent home-made wines, such as gooseberry, sloe, parsnip and dandelion. After this meal the entertainment began: old ballads were sung, humorous stories were told, and two old shepherds would bring out their fiddles and we would finally end by telling ghost stories. This was a very suitable type of closing for it always provided an excellent excuse for we lads to take our girl friends home.

In his classic account of English village life, *Good Neighbours*, Walter Rose tells of the final days of pig, after it had been ringed through its nose by the blacksmith the prevent its damaging rooting habits.

The joys of rooting thus ended, nothing remained but surrender to the blisses of eating and sleeping. To grow fast, and grow fat, made exertion less and less desirable. What need for effort with life so bountifully full? To sleep the sleep of the just was better – with eyes slightly open – emitting melodious snores – and so to wile away the sultry hours of summer; to stretch the long body at ease on the soft straw in the cool shade of the shed, head only at the doorway to sniff the fragrant air from off the cottage garden and the valley beyond. This was the life of the pig.

The days were shortening; already a nip – the foretaste of winter – was in the early morning air, and crimsoned leaves fell, fluttering from the trees. Summer was giving place to winter; the time to transfer the pig from the sty to the cottage was close at hand. Perhaps every owner, when moralising, felt himself a traitor to the animal he had so carefully tended; knowing the tragic end that neared, he was glad of the pig's ignorance. Memory of personal sacrifices gave him further consolation: the daily denials made necessary by the enormous amount of food that the pig had eaten; the extra hours of work on the garden and allotment in producing the potatoes and barley for its food, all hard labour, all freely rendered. Looking at it from that angle he was able to call it a square deal, a realisation of invested capital with interest.

We draw a veil over the act of killing, and ease our minds with the knowledge that more humane methods are now adopted. Dispositions then, as now, were plastic and conformed to the inevitable, but everyone, I believe, was glad when it was over. As children we remained indoors for the worst, and sallied forth to see the pig lying dead on a thin layer of clean wheat straw, with the butcher carefully shaking straws all over its glossy back and tucking wisps between its legs. It looked quite happy.

"A couple of flitches of bacon are worth fifty thousand Methodist sermons and religious tracts. The sight of them upon the rack tends more to keep a man from poaching and stealing than whole volumes of penal statutes, though assisted by the hulks and gibbet. They are the softeners of temper, and promoters of domestic harmony."

William Cobbett, *Cottage Economy*

It was a shame poor Thora had to go but as I was once wisely advised, the animal breeder's best friend is the butcher. She was a nice pig in many ways; a large, tubby and shining example of the Large Black pig, a breed of which I am exceptionally fond. It is true that she showed one or two personality defects in that she was invariably rude and ill-mannered at feeding time, knocking all others out the way and thinking only of herself. But bad behaviour in a pig is not good reason for giving it the chop, so to speak, although her incessant rooting was causing more destruction than could be tolerated. I know that all pigs will root if given the opportunity, but this pig's excavations were more than I could put up with.

But her major defect was in her shape and conformation which seems little excuse for sending her to the butcher but if you are trying to breed animals true to type and keep alive distinguished breeds and their pedigrees, certain defects cannot be allowed. Thora had a dished back which made her look as though she had been ridden by a heavy chap at a rodeo. Her ears did not flop as those of a Large Black pig should, and her only litter consisted of just four piglets which never seemed to thrive or fatten or be distinguished in any way. On the plus side we knew her as a character, had reared her from birth, and suffered her like an unwelcome, but nevertheless slightly loved relation. But taking the pluses and the minuses into account, Thora came out on the losing side.

Eventually, the day will dawn when *your* pig must head towards the butcher. Confront it. Do not flinch, hesitate, or wrap the issue in words which avoid the truth. I have had calls from anxious pig keepers approaching slaughter for the first time, who ask if I can advise them "now that her time has come," or "who do I ring to help me do what . . . er . . . has to be done.. oh dear . . ?" and on it goes. Deliberately and heartlessly I say "Oh, you have a pig ready for the kill. Ring Charlie and he'll fix it. And don't forget to tell him how you want it butchered." No messing, no tiptoeing round the subject: the time has come, you must be brave. I admit the first time is hell, particularly if you have been fattening a single pig and know it well. But if you have been rearing a dozen offspring of one sow you will be more than glad to see the back of them having watched them progress from adorable childhood into objectionable adolescence. A six month old pig is an ill-mannered and unlovable beast.

You may think I am a hard-hearted bastard, but in mitigation let me confess that it was not with great joy that I fed Thora on the morning before the lorry was due to call. At least with a floppy-eared Large Black pig you can easily avoid looking it in the eye. But once she had been loaded and the ramp raised and her final journey had begun, I did not allow myself any remorse. I consider that I had looked after that pig well, given her as good a life as any pig can have and without my help she would not have been there in the first place. All this is, of course, no cast-iron argument for killing, but they are farm animals, bred to be eaten. As the lorry leaves the farm, I only allow myself to look forward to a fine feast. I recommend you do the same.

You have now left the world of farming and you will find you have entered a world of which you may know very little. You have effectively donned the striped apron, grasped the cleaver, and have stepped behind the butcher's counter; a place about which most farmers, and even more consumers, know very little. You are now into butchery. No sooner will your pig have hit the road than the butcher will be on the phone asking "how d' yer want 'er cut?" It is as well to have a ready answer to this question, or admit straight away that you have not a clue. I remember my answer when first asked that question was, "er. . how do you . . . er . . . usually ..?" Pathetic.

To help you, I will tell you what I did with Thora. It is far from being the only thing to do with a pig and there is certainly great pleasure to be had from devising new approaches; but the way I did it and the recipes I used all work, and so it is as good a starting point as any.

To get an idea where the best meat is to be found, imagine a line drawn from the about knee height on the pig's hind leg to the middle of its shoulder. Above the line is the most meat, the juiciest, the tenderest. The further you sink below the line, the more work you are going to have to put into making a decent meal out of whichever piece you choose. For the moment we shall ignore the head.

Think instead of the glorious hind leg. This is not only the basis of what will be our magnificent hams, it will also give us an unmatchable joint of roast leg of pork, crackling as golden as the crown jewels, flesh as juicy as a ripe fruit. But only if your leg of pork has enough fat on it. If you have reared the pig yourself – and a traditional breed of pig at that – you will not be wanting for fat. The problem arises if you have bought a pig which has been farmed efficiently and intensively. You may well find that it is easier to get crackling by roasting an old carpet slipper than by putting a piece of this in the oven.

Do not earmark both your pig's precious legs for the roasting tin. In fact, the great mistake is to have too much of anything, for it is amazing how quickly you will tire of pork chops when you know you have thirty of them standing in the freezer and the use-by-date is fast approaching. Instead, consider your pig in two halves. One half for cooking and roasting, the other half for curing into hams, gammons and bacons. We shall consider the curing later. For the moment, let us ponder Thora's hind leg.

It was a big one and far too large to leave whole unless one had thirty people to feed and a baker's oven in which to roast it; so I asked for it to be cut into joints of between three and four pounds in weight which will feed four people well. Your butcher will then ask if you prefer it left on the bone, or the bone taken out and the meat rolled and tied with string. Suit yourself. Many will say that any joint cooks better with the bone in and this is probably true; but a joint with the bone in is certainly more wasteful when carving. As butchering a carcass is no effort at all to a man who has been doing it all his career, it would not be too much to ask of your butcher to take the leg and give you a joint with the bone in – probably the upper part which is known as the fillet which is the very best of the meat and therefore should be given the best cooking – and the rest of the leg can then be rolled with the bone removed. You may then have that cut into a further couple of joints if the leg were large enough in the first place. Think variety. Try and get as many different joints as you can so that every time you take a piece from the freezer, it is to be eagerly anticipated, and not dreaded.

Roast pork, if good pig-meat to start with and properly roasted, cannot be bettered. It is said, by Charles Lamb in his *Dissertation Upon Roast Pig* , that it was Bo-Bo, the son of a Chinese swineherd, who first discovered the joys of roast pork and crackling after he accidentally burnt down his father's house in which lived a litter of young piglets. Bo-Bo, it is said, bent down to touch one of the piglets to see if it was still alive and this was how he made his discovery:

" . . .he burnt his fingers, and to cool them he applied them in his

booby fashion to his mouth. Some of the crumbs of the scorched skin had come away with his fingers, and for the first time in his life (in the world's life indeed, for before him no man had known it) he tasted . .
."

To say that this method of cooking "caught on" is something of an understatement for the pig-house was rebuilt and then ignited when the next litter of piglets achieved roasting age. Like all good ideas, others were swift to copy:

"The thing took wing, and now there was nothing to be seen but fire in every direction. Fuel and pigs grew enormously dear all over the district . . . People built slighter and slighter every day, until it was feared that the very science of architecture would in no long time be lost to the world."

We do not know for certain how long it took for the realisation to dawn that one did not need to torch the kitchen in order to roast the pig. But the debate still rages about the best way to achieve crackling on a piece of pork.

It would appear that cooking temperature plays an important part in the process of producing fine crackling. If the joint is roasted too hot, the skin will merely burn. If too long and too cool, you will merely end up with soggy, leathery, fried skin. So cook your joint gently to start with, and then up the heat to allow the skin to crackle. The fat will by now have melted and flooded towards the outside of the joint ready and waiting for the intense heat that can crisp and bubble it. Do not be tempted to cover the meat while it is cooking for the steam will then simply sodden the skin and it will never crackle. Whether you should baste or not, or whether salt rubbed into the skin helps, is also a matter of debate.

Some of the finest roast pork I remember eating was cooked by my grandmother in the most modest of post-war gas ovens. Her secret was to allow the meat to cook through and then bring the entire joint to the open coal fire which she had tended throughout the morning so that it was cruelly red and hot, and not at all flaming. Then, like a steelworker before an open furnace, she would sit as long as she could bear it with the joint on the end of a toasting fork, watching the fat bubble and spit and turn from a dull treacle colour to a rich golden blaze. Then we ate it with roast potatoes and dark gravy browned with a little burnt sugar and I cannot remember a better meal.

But roasting on a spit was the way it was always done and when the kitchen range was invented it was thought by many to be the end of good roast meat. Strictly speaking, it was not roasting, for cooking in an oven is technically baking. In *The Cookery of England* Elizabeth Ayrton writes:

". . . with the development of the cooking stove and the 'range', spits went out of use and the 'taste of fire' went with them. Joints of meat were worse cooked than ever before in a country noted for the pleasure it took in the excellence and abundance of its meat. Housewives, cooks, even those who called themselves chefs, put joints to cook in pans containing too much fat of an inferior quality which could only give an unpleasant flavour to the outside of the meat and make it soggy, lacking its crisp light skin."

The following method, taken from *English Recipes* by Sheila Hutchins, seems to be a good compromise which can be achieved without the necessity of constructing some kind of mediaeval spit in front of one's fire place.

TO ROAST PORK Allow 25 mins per lb and 25 minutes over in a pre-heated, fairly hot oven (375F Mk 5) If the meat weighs less than 3 lb allow 25 mins per lb and 40 minutes over. The leg is best raised on a grid in the baking tin to prevent the under-crackling from frying in the dripping and becoming inedible. Greaseproof paper or foil could be wrapped round the thin end of the leg to prevent it from becoming dry before the plump part is cooked.

The rind must of course be scored before roasting so that the meat can be carved neatly when cooked. If this is done deeply enough the fat runs and bastes the meat in cooking. Normally, the butcher scores the crackling though some cooks prefer to do it at home. The best crackling comes from joints with a good layer of fat beneath it. Loins are better for this than the leg. The crackling should be well rubbed with salt before cooking to make it crisp; some cooks also rub it with lemon juice, getting it well down into the incisions, for the same purpose.

To dish the roast pork: having placed the joint on a hot dish pour the surplus fat gently out of the tin, add a little water to the remaining juices and, if liked, some Worcester Sauce. Let it boil rapidly, stirring, over a fierce heat till the liquid is somewhat reduced. This makes for a good thin gravy, far more suitable than the modern packaged concoctions which ruin English roasts.

Let us now turn our eyes away, if we can, from the glories of the leg and cast a glance at the loin. Many will say that this is an even finer piece of the meat than the leg, and certainly can be relied upon to produce even better crackling, for a pig carries more fat on its back than it does around its leg. It would be a great shame if you were to let your butcher simply hack this into chops. By all means have some, perhaps the ones from nearer the back of the pig which may contain a fine piece of kidney, but insist he leaves you a loin joint which can either be left with the bone intact, or boned and rolled, and even stuffed.

While we are on the subject of chops, a chop from a decently-fed and sufficiently fat pig will be a joy in itself, simply fried or preferably grilled on a rack to allow the excess fat to drain away giving, in one simple slice, the crunch of crackling – if the grill is hot enough – and a bite of fat, tasty and digestible enough to kill for. This might be a good point at which to reunite the traditional bedfellows of pork and apples. In cider-making parts of the country, it is my guess that surplus or bruised apples which were not suitable for pressing would be slung at the pigs. Certainly pigs adore apples and the Gloucester Old Spot is a pig renowned for its orchard scavenging skills. It is said that if pigs are fed on large quantities of apples as they approach the kill, the flesh will taste all the sweeter. Possibly.

Instead, try this. Having seasoned your chops and browned them quickly in butter over a high heat, remove them from the pan into a baking dish. You can sprinkle them with a few breadcrumbs if you wish. Fry some apple rings in the same pan in which you have just fried the chops and place then atop the chops which will now be serenely lying beneath their dusting of crumbs. You now make a sort of gravy with the deliciously burnt bits of apple and pork which will be sticking to the pan; but instead of making the sauce with stock, try double cream. Add it to the pan and scrape away with enough vigour to lift every nugget of flavour that has stuck to the pan, and as soon as the cream comes to the boil, pour over the chops. Bake till the chops are done, about a quarter of an hour.

While we are in this nether region of loin and leg, we must consider the marinade; the ritual soaking in fruits, juices and spices which can add subtlety to any joint of meat. I confess to not being very skilled at detecting the effects of delicate marinades but I know that whenever I have eaten a joint that has been treated in this way, I am always deeply impressed by the results. We must look to the east to find true inventiveness in the matter of marinading. It appears that to these robust palates, each a connoisseur of a fine piece of pork, a mere dangling of the joint in a little red wine for a few hours will not do. Try this for a good soaking, from Jean Redwood's *Russian Food*:

Marinade your joint or chops overnight or even for two or three days in the following:

Equal quantities of vinegar, water and red wine with half this amount of vegetable oil. Add herbs such as bay leaf, tarragon, parsley stalks, plus onion rings, peppercorns and salt. Cook your joint or chops in the usual way with the marinade. To finish off, press grated toasted rye breadcrumbs, mixed with the zest of a lemon, into the meat and brown for a further ten minutes. Remove the fat from the gravy, using a separator, or put a bowl of the gravy in the refrigerator for it to harden before removing. Add the lemon juice to this, and if you like a thicker gravy mix cornflour with a few spoonfuls of cold water and then boil it up with the meat juices. The pork dish is usually served with redcurrant sauce flavoured with cinnamon.

It is pretty strong stuff, but on reflection not quite as robust as one might like. I am of the school that thinks there is no point going to a great deal of trouble unless the reward is ample. So, let us turn to *Old Polish traditions in the Kitchen and at the Table* by Maria Lemnis and Henryk Vitry. Here they describe the preparation of a "rump of boar" but we may employ a little licence and try the same recipe with a weighty leg, or loin. They do warn that the joint must not weigh less than 4 lb "in order to avoid disappointments at the table."

Place the meat in a stoneware pot and cover with boiling marinade consisting of ¾ pint of dry red wine, the juice of one lemon, a thin slice of lemon rind, 2 sliced onions, 10 grains of pepper and pimento (allspice), 2 cloves, 20 dried juniper berries, one small clove of garlic, one small bay leaf, a piece of ginger (or 1/3 teaspoon powdered ginger) and 10-12 prunes. A piece of carrot, parsley and celeriac cut into slices may also be added.

Marinate the meat for 2-3 days, the rump for the shorter and the haunch for the longer period. In an oven pan heat intensely 2 oz lard and into this place the salted meat, drained of the marinade, and brown it on all sides. Now place one large sliced onion and prunes taken out of the marinade into the pan. Cover the pan and place in a hot oven. During the roasting, from time to time pour a tablespoon of the marinade over the meat. After about two hours the roast should be just right. Now dust with 1 tablespoon flour and brown in an oven in an uncovered pan.

Season the concentrated sauce in the pan (there should be no more than ½ pint of it) with a tablespoon of rose hip preserve, a pinch of ground cinnamon and, if desired, a little sugar and salt. Thin out the thick sauce to its proper consistency by adding 2-4 tablespoons of marinade and rub through a sieve when cooked. It should be sweet-sour, spicy, but with the roast flavour predominant. Pour this sauce over the carved meat, which has been placed on a platter.

Leaving the rump, leg and loin behind, we arrive at a tricky part of the pig, which is the shoulder. There is nothing wrong with the meat in any way and I have eaten joints of boned and rolled shoulder of pork and not been able to taste any difference between that and leg. It is vastly cheaper too, and since much shop-bought pork these days is too lean, the act of boning and rolling puts some of that fat back inside the joint where it is sorely needed. So my advice, and what I did with Thora, is to have the shoulder boned and rolled and then halved. One half can be roasted, or marinaded if you wish. It is also an ideal joint for stuffing and if you feel brave enough, you can undo your butcher's careful knot-work and stuff the shoulder with, say, a robust mixture of herbs such as sage and thyme, parsley and garlic held together in breadcrumbs with an egg. Roll the joint and tie together, and you have it.

With the other half of the shoulder, I like to try something interesting and if the time of year is right – if you are being strictly traditional you will have killed your pig in November – you should make a pork pie. I could write another book about the eclipsing of the traditional pork pie by its modern mass-produced relation, but many have been there before me. Suffice it to say that its decline has taken place hand in hand with the slow depreciation in the quality of pork. Unless you have been to one of the few proud pork pie makers who still turn out prime examples of the species, you may never have tasted the real thing. I do not believe that I ever have, for pork pie is one of those tastes that develops with age; and in the days when I was in and out of the pork butcher's shop with my grandfather, I would not have given it a second look. By the time I was of an age to fully appreciate a pork pie, the shop and others like it had gone.

Instead came a pinky splodge in a brown greasy crust wrapped in a plastic bag, sweating as if it were fearful of being discovered for the pale imitation that it is. Make your own! Put these perverted snacks behind you and struggle through the hot water crust pastry, the mincing, the teasing from the tin, the praying that it will not collapse, the debate over whether the gelatin is strictly necessary to produce the inner lining of jelly that a good pork pie should have.

The biggest problem in making a raised pork pie, is the raising of it. Allow that to drift to the back of your mind and give your courage time to gel, while you boil bones for the luscious jelly that will fill every nook and cranny of your pie that is not filled with minced, spiced pork. I have to say that I am never offered the bones of my pigs and I have never bothered to ask for them. Unless you need pork stock, which is rare, they seem to take up a huge amount of freezer space for what they are worth. But if you have a pork pie in mind, you will need a few good bones, and possibly a pig's trotter, all adding up to 3 lb in weight. A carrot or two, an onion and perhaps a few cloves should accompany the bones into the stock pot where they should bubble gently for at least two or more hours. Jane Grigson warns against adding salt, and who would dare disagree? When you have bubbled your bones for long enough, strain and then boil the liquid down till you have a pint. Now you add the salt and pepper. If you do not want to go to the trouble of boiling bones, you can use chicken stock and gelatin but your pie will not win any prizes.

All this has given you time to consider whether you will *raise* your pork pie in the traditional manner, or be wooed by the comparative ease with which one can be made in a six inch cake tin with a removable bottom. You do not have to decide yet. Wait till you have your hot-water pastry in your hands and then you can look the enemy full in the eye and make your decision.

Not that the pastry is in any way difficult to make. A pound of plain flour with a pinch of salt is placed in a bowl. Now take 6 oz of lard (the real stuff – no polyunsaturated spreads allowed) and place this in a pan with 8 fl oz of a mixture of equal parts of milk and water. As the liquid heats the lard melts, and as you stir the mixture will come to the boil. I warn you it will boil quickly and so you need to be vigilant, especially as molten lard and hot milk seems to be a mixture with explosive potential. It shoots up the pan as it reaches boiling point like the proverbial rat up the drainpipe. Pour the boiling mixture into the flour and stir till you have a dough, and when it is cool enough to handle knead it lightly. There is no point trying to do anything with it now for it runs in a fashion not unlike lava, and so until it has cooled and pulled itself together it is best left. My guess is that the entire secret of raising a pie is knowing exactly the moment when the pastry is ready for moulding. I have yet to judge it right.

For that reason, it would be unfair of me to recommend that you do anything other than use a small cake tin, or one of those oval-shaped and fluted moulds which are expensive but can give your pie a distinctive shape and aura. I suppose you should grease whichever sort of tin you decide to use but there is so much grease in your pastry that it seems superfluous. When you sense your pastry is firm enough to hold together when rolled, roll it into a circle and then lift it (best of luck) and start to press it into the corner of the mould. It is funny stuff and simply because you have pressed it into one corner it does not mean it will stay there. Also remember to leave enough pastry to make a lid.

You can now think about the filling. If you are regretting not having at least attempted the traditional hand raising, do not let me put you off. I have tried it round a jam jar, a Kilner Jar, and a small saucepan, but the result is always the same. As soon as I try to remove the mould, the pastry slumps like a pair of pale brown trousers which have parted company with their belt. But do not let me put you off. If you have a guaranteed way of doing it, please share it with the rest of us.

Before considering the filling, you must decide in which tradition you wish to make your pie. If you want it pink inside, as a Yorkshire pork pie is supposed to be, then you will need a little unsmoked streaky bacon. If you like your pork pie grey, as was more traditional in the Shire counties, you need simply mince your pork, about 2 lb of it, fairly coarsely, ensuring the meat is fairly lean. You can have up to quarter of the total contents of the pie as fat in order to keep the whole thing moist, but no fattier. To 2 lb of minced pork add a good 2 teaspoons of salt and some black pepper and perhaps a teaspoon of dried sage. There are endless herbs and spices you can add if you wish, such as mace and nutmeg which are commonly used. Now get your hands into it and knead it well to distribute the fat and flavourings. Now pack the pastry with the meat mixture and ensure it fills every corner, and then place the pastry lid on top of it, having remembered to cut a hole in the top for the steam to escape. Have some fun with the decoration, for a pork pie should be a celebratory item to bring to the table, and can take any amount of delicate sculpturing. I like to cut the left over pastry into holly leaves, but that's the way I am. Brush the top of the pie with a little beaten egg and ensure the join between lid and case is secure and leak proof, and you are ready to bake your pie.

The pork takes far longer to cook than the pastry and so I would have a square of tin foil to stop the top burning. Give the pie a good blast of heat (425/mark 7) for about twenty minutes and then turn the heat right down to 350/mark 4 and give it a further three quarters of an hour. During this time, the pork will have started to cook and the fat will be flowing both into the meat and the pastry, which presents you with your next problem.

In order for the pastry to be thoroughly cooked, and to achieve the required brownness all round (which is the mark of a well-cooked pork pie) the half-cooked pie must be removed from the tin. If you have not remembered to use a loose-bottomed tin, you are lost. Let the pie cool for a little and then, as gently as a angel pushing a cobweb through the eye of a needle, ease the pie up from the mould. In fact, I do this by standing the pie tin on a mug and sliding the tin downwards; it eliminates that feeling that the whole thing is going to topple over as it emerges.

If you are lucky, your pie will be intact. If it is, give thanks and do not fiddle with it. I once cooked a pork pie and foolishly thought that a little work with the end of a knife would smoothen a slightly dodgy patch. What I had not realised was that the pie contained a huge reservoir of juice which burst forth as if spouting from a ruptured dam as a direct result of my fiddling. I ended up with a very dry pie. It is said that you hardly need to add any jelly-like juice for there is usually enough moisture in the pie. There seems to be no way of predicting. I have made some juicy pies and some as dry as a sow's back. Either way, do not worry about the filling yet. Brush the whole pie with some more beaten egg and place it, now removed from its tin, back in the oven for another half hour or so. Depending on your oven, you can decide whether to protect the top from further browning. Not till the pie has cooled for at least two hours should you add the jellified stock which can be reheated back to a liquid state and then poured into the pie through a small hole in the crust, with a small funnel, or a steady hand.

And that's it. If you want a pink pie instead of a grey one, you can do the Melton Mowbray trick which I am told is to add a few drops of anchovy sauce to the pork mixture. I have not tried it but it sounds plausible. The Yorkshire Pork Pie can be given its pinkish tinge either by using lightly pickled pork, or more easily by substituting half a pound of pork for half a pound of unsmoked streaky bacon in the meat mixture. Perhaps a teaspoon of dried mustard too.

In Thomas B. Finney's *Handy Guide for Pork Butchers* he gives recipes for several pies, many of which seem to be extinct but are doubtless worthy of resurrection. Unfortunately, the recipes appear to require huge quantities of seasonings but only half an ounce of any one mixture is used to every pound of pie meat. It means that many of the ingredients will be no more than a "good pinch." I will let you do the sums for yourself.

The Nottingham Pie
3 lb gnd white pepper
3 oz cayenne
2 oz nutmeg
2 oz mace
7 lb fine salt

The Liverpool Pie
2 lb gnd white pepper
1 oz ground cinnamon
2 oz ground cayenne
4 ½ lb fine salt

The Yorkshire Pie
3 lb gnd white pepper
3 oz ground cayenne
2 oz ground nutmeg
6 ½ lb fine salt

The Derbyshire Pie
2 lb gnd white pepper
1 oz ground mace
½ oz ground nutmeg
4 lb fine salt

The Manchester Pie
2 lb gnd white pepper
½ oz ground cloves
1 oz ground nutmeg
1 oz ground coriander
1 oz ground mace
4 ½ lbs fine salt

The Lincolnshire Pie
4 lb gnd white pepper
8 oz gnd Jamaican ginger
2 oz fine ground sage
9 ¼ lb fine salt.

Before you go out and order herbs and spice by the pound and salt by the hundredweight, remember, you only need *half an ounce* of the above mixtures to every *pound* of pie meat.

In our journey along the carcass, we have now arrived at the pig's head, which I shall save till later; for the less endearing parts of the pig call for special attention. But from half your pig (remember the other half is to be cured) you should obtain at least one boned and rolled shoulder joint, and enough meat from the same shoulder to make at least a couple of pork pies; you may manage three fine joints from the leg for roasting and marinading; likewise from the loin which has given you the finest of joints, and possibly a few chops too. Now give thanks for all that you have been given and remember the bit we have forgotten – the belly.

Belly pork is not popular these days; even on modern lean pigs it has more fat running through it than any other joint. I remember as a child, granny used to buy it and we devoured it roast but these days it is considered almost waste. But belly-pork slices, lightly pickled, can be fried or baked with a little sugar as was recommended by my Irish farmer friend. Or you can make sausages. There is great satisfaction in making your own bangers; you can make them as meaty as you wish and spend many happy hours juggling with herbs and spices. But these are a book on their own, and a great fiddle if you do not have an electric mixer that squeezes the sausage mixture into the skins for you. So forget sausages and try instead an East Riding Pudding. Since many of my childhood weekends were spent on that part of the Yorkshire coast which fell into the East Riding of Yorkshire, I suppose I should be familiar with this pudding. I confess I got it some time ago from the *Daily Telegraph*. Perhaps it explains why some of the people I met in East Yorkshire seemed unable to move from their seats. This is truly a dish to hold you down to earth.

Having perfected your hot-water pastry while making the pork pie, make another pound of it and line a greased pudding basin. Into the basin, lay strips of streaky belly pork with some onion and a little sage and then a layer of thinly sliced potatoes. You will need a drop of water as well to provide some steam and to stop the whole thing drying out. Roll the remaining pastry to form a lid and steam for a good three hours. Give it good gravy, and apple sauce. And do not be far from your bed, so that you can collapse under its weight.

But there are two sides to every story, and there were certainly two sides to our old sow, Thora. The second half of her I reserved for curing into hams and bacon. This is where we must consider carefully how we proceed. Curing is, in itself, an apparently simple chemical process of preservation but it needs as much care as the most delicate of cooking if you are ever to achieve the finest hams. It is worth remembering what we are trying to achieve in our curing of bacon and ham. I shall take as my text the words of George J. Nicholls, author of *Bacon and Hams* published by the Institute of Certificated Grocers in 1917. So devoted was Mr Nicholls to his subject that a photograph of him appears, opposite the preface, of the author "in fancy dress as a side of bacon, designed by himself, which took the first prize of forty guineas at the Covent Garden Fancy Dress Ball, April 1894".

Nicholls declares:

"All men have an interest in bacon, with the exception, perhaps, of the Jew; and the man of little imagination, but of sound appetitive instincts, who had bacon and eggs for breakfast one morning, and varied the monotony by ordering eggs and bacon the next, was more than justified by the almost unanimous vote of the community – the pig is the true aristocrat of the breakfast table."

We are seeking a ham or bacon of which Nicholls could be proud, which he could lay before his Institute of Grocers without a hint of shame.

But be warned. Word will get round that something special is happening; that very soon there might be bacon in the pan that does not drown in it own milky oozings, but crisps and browns and melts on the tongue. The rumour will also spread that hams are being cured and that luscious slices with ample fat will soon be available. You will soon find you have friends you never knew existed. I advise you not to answer the knock on the door, for William Cobbett in his *Cottage Economy* found unwelcome guests often attend the curing of a pig;

> ... about this time it is more than possible that the Methodist parson will pay you a visit. It is remarked, in America, that these gentry are attracted by the squeaking of the pig, as the fox is by the cackling of the hen. This may be called slander, but I will tell you what I did know to happen. A good honest careful fellow had a spare-rib, on which he intended to sup with his family after a long and hard day's work at coppice-cutting. Home he came at dark with his two little boys, each with a nitch of wood that they carried four miles, cheered with the thought of the repast that awaited them. In he went, found his wife, the Methodist parson, and a whole troop of the sister-hood, engaged in prayer, and on the table lay scattered the clean-polished bones of the spare-rib! Can any reasonable creature believe, that, to save the soul, God requires us to give up the food necessary to sustain the body?

There is no part of the process of consuming the pig which attracts as much mystery and secrecy as the curing of hams. As I found in my travels, curers were always willing to admit how they did it, up to a point. When I asked what they used in their cure they would say, "...

124

the usual, salt, sugar, and a few bits and pieces of my own." Never was I given a full recipe, and never would I press too hard with my enquiries. But it is not all that difficult to discover. If you wish to delve as far as 200BC, you will find that Cator the Censor wrote of the people of Lombardy who salted 4,000 flitches a year, and gave the recipe:

> When you have bought your hams, cut off the hoofs. Take half a peck of roman salt, ground fine for each. Lay salt over the bottom of the tub; then put in a ham, the skin-side looking downwards. Cover it over with salt. Then put another ham on top, taking care that meat does not touch meat. So deal with them all. When you have got them all snug put salt over them, so that no meat is visible, and make the surface level. When they have been in salt for five days take them all out and the salt with them. Then put them in again in reverse order so that those which were before on top are now at the bottom. Cover them over and make them snug in the same way as before. After twelve days at most, take the hams out, rub off all the salt and hang them up in a draught for two days. On the third day wipe them well over with a sponge and rub them with oil. Hang them for two days in the smoke. Then take them down, rub them well with a mixture of oil and vinegar and hang them up in the meat larder.

There is nothing wrong with that. Try it today and it will still work. Indeed, many of the curers I visited, and I think of Richard Woodall in Cumbria, did little more than that. The only drawback is that your ham is likely to be saltier than is common these days.

There is no harm in understanding the process of curing for in my experience it is widely misunderstood. Microbes and micro-organisms living within the meat are what cause it to go rancid, or "off." In order to kill these microbes and ensure a long life for the meat, the environment in which they live must be drastically altered so that they can no longer survive. The easiest way to achieve this is to deprive them of water. If you wrap a piece of pork in salt, you will soon begin to notice a steady dribble of fluid from it. This is the water, not the blood as is often thought, being drawn from the meat by the action of the salt, dehydrating it, and thereby destroying the nasties. That is why Cator the Censor's recipe is as good today as it was then.

But he had an advantage that we do not have in that the "roman salt" which he would have used would have been far less pure than that which we buy today. He did not know how lucky he was, for rough old salt contained not just sodium chloride, but contaminants including naturally-occurring nitrates. When these nitrates come into contact with the bacteria, a series of complex chemical reactions take place the end result of which is that the meat turns bright pink. Without the nitrates, it would turn grey. If you want grey hams, cure only in pure salt. But if you want them to be bright pink you must use nitrates as well. These are usually provided in the form of saltpetre and most modern curing recipes include a small amount of it.

There is a rumour going round that saltpetre cannot be bought from chemists any longer. The accepted wisdom is that this is because it forms the basis of an explosive mixture – as any schoolchild will testify – and so to prevent it falling into the hands of terrorists, it can no longer be bought across the counter. This is not true. The facts of the matter are that any chemist is allowed to sell it to you and there is no law to prevent them. The problem is that chemists no longer carry stocks of such things, but should be able to get it with ease. It would be as well to explain why you want it and make it clear that you need very little of it (you will be using it only by the teaspoon) and you should have no problem. If you try buying it by the sackful you should expect to be asked searching questions. But using nitrates in large quantities is not a good idea anyway for some research suggests they are carcinogenic in large quantities. Do not be put off by any of this for it is probably the case that you would need to eat more ham than the human frame could ever contain before you need fear any ill-effects from the nitrates.

But back to the pig. Ask your butcher to cut it as follows. Remove the leg, which will become the ham (a perfect leg for curing will have the shape of a tennis racquet) and depending on how fine a feast you are considering, you can ask him at this stage to halve, or even quarter it if it is a large pig. He may advise that it be cured whole and then jointed, but if you cannot handle a piece of meat as big as the leg, you will have to insist. Have the loin and the belly cut whole, which will give you the back bacon and the streaky. The shoulder is a bit of a problem for although it makes fine collar bacon, it is large and never as popular as the ham or the gammon. You may decide not to cure the shoulder but use it as yet another piece of pork.

You must now decide if you are going to dry-salt your ham and bacon, or use a brine in which to soak it. Dry-salting will give you a much saltier and more traditional cure; a milder cure will come from the use of a brine, which can also be used to impart subtle flavours to your ham. You can make as much or as little of curing hams as you wish, but I suspect that it is one of those jobs where effort is rewarded. So I will describe five-star treatments, and you can cut corners if you wish.

You will need a fine, old, white porcelain sink if you can find one and can provide some kind of lid for it. I can think of nothing better for curing hams, for it is easily cleaned and the plug-hole comes in useful for allowing the dehydrating fluids to drain away. Alas, I never found one although I met countless builders who told me they had just smashed one up. In the end I settled for a plastic tub. Nor was I ever able to achieve the ideals set out in Thomas B. Finney's *Handy Guide for Pork Butchers, Bacon Curers, Sausage and Brawn Manufacturers, Provision Merchants, & co.* He states:

> Curing should always be carried on in dry, roomy cellars, the windows of which should be so arranged as to allow a strong current of dry, cool air to continually pass through, but which must also admit of their being closed during the extreme cold weather. The walls and ceilings should be well white-washed at least twice every year. The floors should be either flags, concrete, or cement, the latter being always considered the best. The floor should be slightly inclined towards the centre of the cellar, where a good water grid should be fixed to carry off all waste brine, etc. The floor should be well washed about once every month with cold water, to every gallon of which should be added about one ounce of permanganate of potash; this is a powerful disinfectant, and will ensure the cellars being kept cool and sweet all year round.

Well, we can all do our best. We are lucky enough to have a well-ventilated larder and I have always confined my curing to the traditional months of November till the end of March. Providing you can keep the cat at bay, this arrangement seems to work.

The principal ingredient in your dry-salting cure will, of course, be salt. Refined kitchen salt sold with "anti-caking" agents and other additives to ensure free-running will be of no use to you. You must seek out sea-salt, and avoid refined rock salt. You will also need saltpetre to keep your ham rosy. I will not quote recipes from some elderly books for some of these old cures contained enough saltpetre to cure a herd of swine; but they are interesting in that many use cane sugar as well as the salt, it being claimed that the sugar prevents the meat from hardening. Cloves can also be used, as can juniper berries and almost any

127

herb you fancy. But the basic proportions to cure a 12 lb joint of pork are roughly 3 lb of sea salt to which is added an ounce of saltpetre and two ounces of sugar. I would play around and improvise if I were you; curing hams comes from practice and experimentation and you can afford to try different recipes before giving your personal blessing to any one recipe.

The provenance of hams is difficult to understand for I have been given one definitive recipe for a York ham, only to have it contradicted. I can offer Elisabeth Ayrton's view, expressed in *The Cookery of England* – but do not expect everyone to agree:

> York hams are traditionally dry-cured with salt, a little saltpetre and a little brown sugar for three weeks and then smoked over oak sawdust for at least two months. Green Yorkshire hams and Green Westmoreland hams used also to be obtainable, and very fine they could be. They lay for four days in a special sweet cure which was a mixture of common salt, bay salt, saltpetre and black pepper with treacle poured all over. They were turned and rubbed twice a week for a month and then soaked for twenty four hours in cold water and hung up to dry.
>
> Suffolk hams are sweet-cured but smoked. Honey was considered more penetrating than either sugar and treacle, and was preferred for this reason in some districts. It must, of course, have been used in early cures before sugar was available, when a certain sweet flavour to alleviate the general saltiness of winter meat was particularly prized.

Providing you proceed along the following general lines, I find that you cannot go wrong. Take the piece of pork to be cured and rub it well with the salt mixture you plan to use. Enjoy the massage, working it into the flesh making sure that the meat and skin are well covered. Place a layer of the salt on the bottom of the bucket, crock, sink, or whatever you are using, and place the ham upon it flesh down, skin up, and pack the rest of the salt over and around it till you have buried it from sight, and pressed the salt firmly to ensure that no part of the pork is in contact with anything other than salt. You will need some kind of clean and sterilised lid which can press down on the salt, and then you can forget it for at least two weeks. You can turn it if you must, but it will hardly be necessary. If the temperatures are cool enough, two months would not be too long to leave it. Do not be surprised to open the crock and find your ham slopping around in water; the juices from the meat will have dissolved the salt to produce a brine.

A brine-cured ham is easier, and, I suspect more reliable. You still need to ensure everything is scrupulously clean before you start, and you need only contemplate it in the cooler months of the year, but somehow there seems less chance for error.

The curing of a ham in brine has been set down for centuries, and the method you employ need not be any different from that in use a couple of centuries ago. With brine cures you can indulge in flourish and experimentation, curing with ale, or stout, treacle or honey. Living in Suffolk I have always been inclined towards the Suffolk cure which gives a deliciously sweet ham or bacon with a black rind that causes the unfamiliar eater to give it a second look, whereas those who have tasted the Suffolk cure before will know that the black rind merely conceals great pleasures yet to come. The recorder of oral history in Suffolk was George Ewart Evans and in his *Ask the Fellows Who Cut the Hay* he writes:

> The ham was given first a dry salt-bath; salt was rubbed into it and it was left in the pot, covered with salt, for seven days. At the end of this period the ham was taken out; the ham pot was emptied of the salt and a sweet pickle was made in it. This consisted of two pounds of real black treacle; two pounds of real dark brown sugar; one quart of thick beer or stout – this, at least, was Prissy Savage's formula. The beer or stout was heated and then poured over the sugar and treacle. After the ham had been thoroughly drained of the salt it would be placed in the pot and the mixture poured over it and then rubbed well into it. A big stone was placed on top of the ham so that every part of it would be covered by the pickle. It was left in the pickle or sweet brine for about six weeks; but every day it would be turned – flesh side up one day, skin side the next. When the six weeks were up, it was taken out, branded with the owner's initials – a blacksmith-made iron was usually the implement – and sent off to be dried.

This is the simplest of cures that I can imagine, and is infallible. My most delicious hams have been cured this way. Needless to say, there are many local variations and although Finney lists a different cure for almost every pig-producing county in Britain, I doubt that few still survive in their own locality. Here are a selection to try:

The Berkshire Cure

For hams of about 16lb, ½ lb of coarse moist sugar, ½ lb of common salt, 1 oz saltpetre, 1 oz bay salt, 1 oz of ground black pepper. Dissolve over a slow fire and put the paste on the fleshy part of the ham as hot as the hand can bear it. When the paste is dissolved, baste twice daily for a month. Wipe well and dry off.

The Buckinghamshire Cure (for bacon)

Rub over each flitch 2 oz of finely pulverised saltpetre, especial care being taken to apply a larger quantity to the parts whence the ham and the shoulder have been removed. The flitches are then placed for ten to twelve hours upon the salting form, and a mixture of 7 lb of salt and 1¼ lb of coarse moist sugar is heated in a frying pan and so stirred as to attain a uniform temperature. The flitches are rubbed all over with this mixture while hot, and then placed the one upon the other in a salting pan, when the brine immediately begins to form. They are well basted and rubbed with the brine, and turned twice a week, the under flitch being placed uppermost at each turning, and at the end of four weeks they are hung up to dry and afterwards smoked.

The Cumberland Cure (please note that this recipe gives quantities for the curing of a whole pig)

A typical Cumberland recipe for a large pig consists of ½ cwt of salt, 6 to 8 lb of demerara sugar, and from 1½ to 2 lb of saltpetre. The hams are rubbed thoroughly with the salt at intervals of four to five days, and the other ingredients added after the second application of the salt, and the bacon smoked after the lapse of another week.

The Hampshire Cure

The hams and the flitches are laid on a cool stone floor, sprinkled with salt, and left for eight to ten hours. After allowing the brine to run off freely by turning them on edge for a time, the skin side of the flitch is rubbed thoroughly with salt, the shanks being stopped with salt and saltpetre. Some curers put the sides into a "silt" of strong brine, after which they are taken out and dry-salted on a bench for from 14 to 21 days, according to the size of the flitches. The flitches are stacked on a cool stone floor, rind downwards, one on top of the other, and at the end of about three days their positions are reversed, the bottom flitch being brought to the top and the top to the bottom. This process is repeated at intervals about six times, and subsequently all the stale briny salt is rubbed off and each flitch is well covered with fresh bran, after which it is hung in the drying room for two or three weeks.

The Lancashire Cure

The side of bacon is cut into three pieces – ham, flitch and shoulder. The rind of each is well rubbed with fine dry salt, the pieces being then placed on a stone slab sprinkled with salt. The curing of the flitch is effected by applying a thin covering of salt, a slight sprinkling of saltpetre, a handful or so of granulated sugar, and finally another sprinkling of salt. The flitch is then left for four days, when the rind is again rubbed with salt, a very thin layer of which is also sprinkled over the surface. In eight to ten days from the commencement of curing the salt is brushed from the flitch, which is then hung up to dry for ten to 14 days, and finally covered with fine muslin and stored in a cool place.

The ham and shoulder are treated in the same way as the flitch, but are left in salt 14 to 21 days, and sprinkled with salt at intervals of four to five days. The ham especially should be disturbed as little as possible.

The Warwickshire Cure

The salting trough is made in readiness to receive the flitches and hams by sprinkling a layer of coarse salt on the bottom. A flitch is placed rind downwards, the rind being well rubbed with salt. Salt is next rubbed in well on the top side, and if there be any bones or lean parts, a little saltpetre is rubbed in before the common salt. Saltpetre not only opens the pores to receive the salt, but gives the meat a proper colour and flavour. When the rubbing is accomplished, a liberal sprinkling of salt is spread over the flitch. Then the second flitch is placed rind downwards on the first, and dressed on both sides in exactly the same way.

The hams are lightly dressed first on the rind side with salt, then on the other side with saltpetre, especially round the base, where curing is more difficult. Next, salt and saltpetre mixed are well rubbed in. Lastly, common salt is freely besprinkled over the whole surface. The second ham is placed over the first, rind downwards, as with flitches. Odd bits of the pig, such as jowls, feet, hocks, and so forth, are salted in a similar way and put in the trough, or in a second one, and the curing is completed so far.

About 4 oz of saltpetre may be used for a pig of 15 score, mostly for the hams, but while common salt may be used freely enough, saltpetre may not, and should be applied in a finely pulverised state to make it prove as effectual in its limited quantity as may be.

In ten days time the flitches and hams are turned over and well rubbed on both sides with fresh salt. In three weeks they should be set upright to drain for two to three hours, and then be hung up to dry in a moderately warm place, such as a kitchen, with a temperature of from 60 to 65F. When partially dried, the hams should be put in bags and allowed to hang up till required for use.

The Wiltshire Cure

A pickle is made with 1 quart of strong beer, ½ lb of treacle, ½ lb of coarse sugar, 1 oz coriander seed, 2 oz juniper berries, 1 oz pepper, 1 oz of allspice, 1 oz of saltpetre, ½ oz of salt prunelle, and a good handful of common salt. These are well pounded together, and when heated, poured over the hams, well rubbed in, and turned every day for a fortnight.

The flitches are sprinkled with salt and left to drain for twenty-four hours, then the following ingredients mixed for a pig of 8 score: 1 ½ lb of coarse sugar, 1 ½ lb of bay salt, 6 oz of saltpetre, and 4 lb of common salt. The mixture is rubbed well into the bacon daily for a month, turning the flitches every day, after which it is dried off and smoked for about ten days."

You may be confused by references to "a pig of 8 score", for example. A score was, as you might guess, 20 lb. The curing recipes also refer to Sal Prunella which can be used in addition to the saltpetre. Sal Prunella is now known less romantically as E251 (saltpetre is E252) and is a form of nitrite. In the curing process, the nitrate in saltpetre is converted into nitrite which gives the cured meat the pink colour. Adding nitrites from the beginning of the curing process gives the curing a kick start. But for home-curing, speed should not be a consideration. You have gone to the trouble of giving your pig a long slow maturing while it was alive, at least allow it the dignity of an unhurried cure in the brine tub.

If all this is intimidating – and I admit that a certain amount of courage is needed to cure a ham for there is always an underlying suspicion that your piece of meat is lying there, turning poisonous, in a bowl of salty swill – I can recommend a man who will solve all your problems, take you safely through the pain barrier of your first cure, and give you sufficient confidence to attempt curing recipes of your own. He is Don

Bateman of the Home Farm Sausage Company and I give his address and number at the end of this book. Not only will he supply ready-made cures, but casings for sausages and salamis. He has the equipment for mincing and stuffing and, most ingenious of all, a smoker no larger than a dustbin which I cannot recommend too highly.

Which brings us to the burning question: do you smoke your ham and bacon, or eat it green? I would vote for smoked. I adore the aromas that the smoking traps within the ham and releases into the kitchen when the ham is cooked. But it masks the subtlety, of that there is no doubt. So if you are the sort who likes their palate to be teased and tormented by the reticent intricacies of, say, Parma ham, you will not be one for the robust smack in the face that a smoked ham can give you.

Smokers are worse, or at least as bad as ham curers, for hiding their secrets. They will tell you that the secret is in the temperature, or the mixture of the woods they burn, or how long they smoke for, or that the fire has been lit by the hand of a virgin, or that they use the same matches their grandfather always used. In order to dispel some of the hazy clouds of confusion that surround the smoking of ham, let us consider briefly the science. I can do no better than offer you Harold McGee's assessment of the smoking process from his book, *On Food and Cooking* which explains in scientific terms, almost every culinary process:

> Smoking is another venerable preservation technique which is actually a kind of slow, low-temperature cooking. But it is also a chemical treatment. Smoke is a very complex material, with upward of 200 components that include alcohols,acids, phenolic compounds, and various toxic, sometimes carcinogenic substances. The toxic substances inhibit the growth of microbes, the phenolics retard fat oxidation, and the whole complex imparts the characteristic flavour of wood to the meat. Salt curing and smoking are often combined to minimise the fat oxidation that salt encourages. A recipe for ham that has come down to us in the Latin cookbook of Apicius uses this double treatment: it directs the cook to salt the meat for 17 days, dry it for 2 in the open air, oil it and smoke for 2 days, and then store it in a mixture of oil and vinegar.

If you can find the space to have a smokehouse of your own, then without doubt you can find great pleasure from smoking your own hams, sausages, fish, game and especially chicken which is a fine dish. It is a pity the privy at the bottom of the garden is an architectural form that has drifted into extinction, for a converted outside lav makes a fine smokehouse and needs little in the way of conversion. I imagine it would not be impossible for the building to lead a double life and be lavatory as well as occasional smoke-house, so if you happen to be the owner of one of these fine buildings you may not want to rule out the option of an occasional lavatorial use.

Instead, you could follow the smokehouse-building suggestions of Robert Henderson, a Scottish farmer of Broomhill, near Annan, who in 1814 wrote *A Treatise on the Breeding of Swine and the Curing of Bacon*. Attempting to smoke his hams by the method that was by then traditional, which was by hanging them in a chimney, he encountered enormous problems and eventually decided to build a smokehouse of his own:

> I practised for many years the custom of carting my flitches and hams through the country to farm-houses, and used to hang them in their chimneys and other parts of the house to dry, some seasons to the amount of 500 carcasses. This plan I soon found was attended with a number of inconveniences, having to take along with the bacon pieces of timber, to fix up in the different houses, for the purposes of hanging the flitches and hams. For several days after they were hung up, they poured down salt and brine upon the women's caps, and now and then a ham would fall down and break a spinning wheel, or knock down some of the children; which obliged me to purchase a few ribbons, tobacco & c., to make up the peace. But there was a still greater disadvantage attending this mode; the bacon was obliged to hang until an order came for it to be sent off, which being at the end of two or three months, and often longer, the meat was overdried in most places, and consequently lost a good deal of weight. This method is practised at this day in Dumfriesshire. People in general are so partial to old customs, that it is nearly impossible to remove them.
>
> About twenty years ago, to prevent these disadvantages, I contrived a small smoke-house, of a very simple construction. It is about twelve feet square, and the walls are 7 feet high. One of these parts requires six joists across, one close to each wall, the other laid four asunder at proper distances. To receive five rows of flitches, they must be laid on top of the wall. A piece of wood, strong enough

to bear the weight of one flitch of bacon, must be fixed across the belly end of the flitch by two strings, as the neck end must hang downwards. The piece of wood must be longer than the flitch is wide, so that each end may rest upon a beam. They may be put so near to each other as not to touch. The width of it will hold 24 flitches in a row, and there will be five rows, which will contain 120 flitches. As many hams my be hung at the same time above the flitches, contrived in the best manner one can. The lower end of the flitches will be within 2½ or 3 feet of the floor, which must be covered 5 or 6 inches thick with sawdust, which must be kindled at two different sides. It will burn, but not cause any flame to injure the bacon. The door must be kept close, and the hut must have a small hole in the roof, so that part of the smoke may ascend. That lot of hams and bacon will be ready to pack up in a hogshead to send off in eight or ten days, or a little longer if required, with very little loss of weight. After the bacon is salted, it may lie in the salthouse as described until an order is received, then immediately hang up to dry.

I found the smokehouse to be a great saving, not only in the expense and trouble of employing men to cart and hang it through the country, but it did not lose nearly so much weight by this process.

It can be easier than this. I have already mentioned Don Bateman and his Home Farm Smokers, imported from America. For those who like to buy off the shelf complete with instruction book and starter kit – which includes everything bar the matches – this cannot be bettered. The more adventurous will spend days hacking away at an oil drum with saws and hammers, or rasping holes in wooden barrels in order to achieve the same effect. Finney gives us a good account of a simple smoker, and how to get the best out of it:

Another method of smoking a ham or flitch is by suspending it in an upturned cider cask or large barrel. In this case a hole is dug in the ground and an old bucket containing a little live coal or red-hot cinders placed on the bottom, with sawdust covering. A little air must be admitted to the fire, and to assist this, a few holes may be knocked in the sides of the pail. When the sawdust smoulders and throws off volumes of smoke without any fear of ignition the barrel containing the bacon may be placed over the hole. It will be necessary to raise the cask a little above the level of the ground, so as to enable the pail and its contents to be controlled and the sawdust prevented from bursting into flame, and this can be done by resting the barrel on some bricks, the space being built quite close so that the smoke from the smouldering sawdust may ascend through the cask. A more elaborate smoke stove can be constructed if so desired, and plenty of good smoked meat is producd in this manner, which is a convenient form of smoking where only one or two flitches are to be treated. A simple and effective arangement by means of which breakfast bacon can be smoked in six to eight hours is made in the following manner: both ends are removed from an ordinary flour or apple cask, and a moveable cover is provided for the top,made either of boards, an old oilcloth, or a tight blanket. A short trench is dug in which is laid a length of old stove pipe. A larger excavation is then made, in which a pan of burning chips (oak) can be placed. This is covered by a tightly fitting plank. One end of the stove pipe communicates with the excavation, over which the other end of the barrel is placed, and the earth banked up around the bottom of the barrel and over the stove pipe to keep it all tight. The meat may be suspended from a stick laid across the top of the cask, and then all covered tightly with an oilcloth or blanket. On placing the pan of burning chips into the space provided, the smoke passes through the stove pipe into the barrel, filling it with dense, cool smoke.

There are two important points here. One relates to the temperature of the smoke, the other to the wood that you burn. It is essential that the smoke is not hot enough to melt the fat and start a cooking process. The smoke needs to cool which seems to happen quite quickly if it has to travel any distance. In Bateman's smokers, you simply add a tall collar (about 18 inches) to the smoking bin which seems enough (but only just enough) to drop the temperature of the smoke below that at which it could start to cook the ham.

As far as wood is concerned, there are ample opportunity for experiment here too. Avoid resinous woods such as pine for you will merely end up with an inedible and tarred ham. But oak, beech and especially apple can give fine flavours to ham and are worth a try.

To get an idea of a professional smoker at work, I went to Richardson's Smokehouse in Orford, on the Suffolk coast. Orford is almost a coastal town but its watefront, which is in fact the River Ore, is separated from the sea by a spit of mobile shingle, called Orfordness.

This is a land of marshes, wide vistas and open skies where the smell of the sea never leaves the air and despite it having become less of a fishing town and more of a tourist trap, it still has the feel of being a community that dabbles its feet in the water. The river and its creeks has been famous for some years now for their oysters, and Pinney's Oysterage Restaurant in particular. Behind this restaurant is where Steve Richardson has chosen to build his smokehouse. It was a cold January morning when I called; a brisk northerly wind fresh off the saltings cut through the town and blew the smoke from the smokehouse across the roof of the neighbouring houses as if it were trying to smoke them too. In the kitchen, Steve and his partner Veronica were having an amiable sort of row about something or other, mackerel were being washed in a huge sink, pheasants and duck were swilling around in brine tubs, and everytime the kitchen door opened a blast of escaping oak smoke from the smokehouse next door filled the room. "Shut the door," cried Veronica, "you'll smoke us out."

"My grandfather, Frank Berrett, built the smokehouse," says Richardson, "but I don't remember too much about it. Frank was a grand old boy. He was the local slaughterman, and the baker. He was a fisherman too. I can remember sticking my head in the smokehouse once, when I was very young, and not being able to work out what the smell was. Of course, it was the oak. I know that now. I can remember the squealing when he killed pigs and we all used to wait around for the pig's bladder and blow it up and play football." As he spoke, he was turning the pages of an old photograph album and as I moved across and stood over him,the oak smoke rose from him as pungently as from any kipper.

"I did a spell working on the oil rigs. Then I was out of work. There used to be a folk night on a Sunday at the Butley Oyster (a local pub) and I used to smoke a bit of mackerel and stand outside the pub selling it. That's how my smoking business started. It wasn't easy. I used the old smokehouse to start with, till the door fell off. I used to boil the hams in a Burco boiler! Can you imagine it? With a friend (Colin Buck) we designed a smoker but I never learnt anything off anybody, I learnt it all myself. When I started, I used to hang the kippers on the hot side and I couldn't work out why, when I went in the next morning, all I had left were heads hanging from the hooks. Too hot, you see."

Bravely ignoring the possibility of a tongue-lashing from Veronica, we opened the kitchen door allowing more oak smoke to seep in, and took the few paces to the lean-to smokehouse. It was the size of a pair of outside lavatories, built side by side with two doors which were a tight fit, but not smoke tight. Thick lumps of tar, deposited by the escaping smoke, slithered slowly down the doors. Richardson donned a triangular woolly hat, stained with tar and smoke, and opened the door. A wall of oak smoke fell towards us and as it cleared, the simple burner could be seen in the shiny blackness of the smokehouse. It was no larger than half an oil drum with a vent at the bottom to control the draught, and a lid with holes which, by turning, would allow the wood to blaze, or smoulder to produce smoke.

"I always use oak. Green as hell. There's no thermometer, no temperature chart. It's all done on the nose. A smell will just drift across and I'll think to myself, "yes, that's done." On the hot side of the smoke house sat a dozen chickens, a score of partridge. Through a letter box in the wall seeped surplus smoke, cooling as it went, and here would hang hams – if he had the room for them – or sausages, prawns, kippers, or even a Stilton cheese.

There is not a lot to it but, I suspect, much to get wrong and experience counts. Having successfully smoked at home and knowing the pleasure that the results have given, I would recommend anyone to have a go. Do not try a ham first, it is too valuable. Instead, hot smoke a chicken for eight hours, or so; perhaps a loin of lamb. Then work your way to a crescendo and give a ham a long, slow smoking for two or three days. It may require effort. You might have to rise from your bed to tend the smoke, but the rewards will be ample.

If you are still wavering and wondering if the curing and smoking of a ham is worth all the trouble, be inspired by an account I read of the curing of hams in North Carolina, USA. In particular, Uncle Billy's ham, renowned througout the state. Joel Bourne, remembering Christmas, writes of his uncle and his hams:

> Reigning over the sideboard like King Solomon on his throne was a ham cured by Uncle Billy. Deep red on the inside, covered with cloves and a mahogany glaze of molasses and brown sugar on the outside, its aroma filled the dining room. I remember nearly transparent slices, rimmed with thin strips of fat, on a white dinner plate. With my mouth watering and my eyes already feasting, my ears turned deaf to my mother's warnings not to eat too much because "it would give us children bad dreams." (After one Christmas ham-eating binge, legend has it that my cousin Henry

awoke among ripped sheets and tossed blankets.) This was strong stuff, I was told – an acquired, grown-up taste, like okra or good bourbon.

Needless to say, Uncle Billy had firm views about the smoking of his prize hams:

Good smoking weather, says Uncle Billy, is like good duck-hunting weather. "I want it to be miserable, damp and cold." But the secret that distinguishes his cured hams from others is the wood he uses for smoking. In the summer when he prunes his fruit trees, Uncle Billy saves all the pruning down to the smallest twig. He has peach and pear trees, but apple wood is his favourite, and he makes sure he has several armfuls. The day before he's ready to smoke, Uncle Billy goes into the woods and fells a hickory sapling as big round as your thigh and cuts it into one-foot lengths. The next day, at seven in the morning, he starts a small fire in the fire-pit, using newspaper and the fruitwood kindling. (Any other starter would taint the meat.) He stays with it all day, adding wood and adjusting the fire until he goes to bed that night.

"Once I get the fire going, I get it hot as hell," he says. "I wait till it burns down. Then I put the green wood on the fire. That's when the smoke starts." The idea in smoking is not to cook the meat but to let the smoke enhance its flavour.If the fat starts to drip, then the fire is too hot. The smoke is the important thing; that's why the smokehouse is well ventilated. The ham will be blond when it comes in, with a clear white skin. Uncle Billy smokes it until it turns a rich mahogany colour. Then his part of the process is over: the rest is up to the meat and time.

The pig, if I am not mistaken,
Supplies us sausage, ham and bacon.
Let others say his heart is big–
I call it stupid of the pig.

The Pig, Ogden Nash

We have been very brave, so far. With great fortitude and self-control we have come to terms with the rearing of pigs, the killing, and then the cooking of them. But we have one more hurdle to jump. We have to face up to the fact that pigs do not consist just of tasty, attractive joints, easily cooked and consumed. There are parts of the pig which we would rather forget, or feed to the dog, or tuck away at the bottom of the freezer till they have been there for long enough for us to feel conscience-free about throwing them out. Face up to them now: the pig's head, cheek, liver, kidney, lites, chitterlings, rind, blood, lungs, trotters and pluck. It is difficult to know where to begin.

In *Handy Hints to Pork Butchers* from which I have already quoted, the author starts with the head. As the book is intended for professionals, it starts its chapter on the pig's head in a robust and unsentimental way such that anyone who is approaching a pig carcass for the first time will run a mile:

"Take a good sized pig's head, with the snout uncut, and a large collar cut right on to the shoulder. The bone must be left in the mouth so as to keep it in good shape. Sew the mouth up with string, and put the head for three days in strong pickle . . ."

Like the pickle, I fear this is all too strong for us. But brawn is a truly great dish, if you do not ponder too long on its ingredients. Brawn, incidentally, is a word having similar roots to "brawny" or muscular, which a good brawn should be. For a proper brawn you will need half a pig's head and you must have the brain and eyeballs removed – the fainthearted can ask their butcher to do this. If you have the trotters, you can use two of those and the tail if it is to hand. A little shin of beef, the muscular yet richly flavoured meat from the beast's leg, will add to the brawniness, and apart from salt and pepper, you will want mace, ginger and nutmeg, but cloves and bay leaf would season just as well. A few drops of lemon oil will also sharpen all the flavours.

Using a teaspoon of all the seasonings, plus an onion, and half a pound of the beef shin, put all the ingredients in a large pan, cover with water and bring to the boil. You must boil till everything is tender. It may take five hours. After this time the meat should fall away from the bones. If it does not, it is not cooked.

You can forget gristle, skin and any huge lumps of fat and simply drain the juices from the meat and chop the meat as finely as you wish. Some people like lumps of meat in their brawn, others prefer something closer to paté. Boil the juices till they have reduced by half, strain this over the meat in a bowl and leave to set overnight. Next day, with a slice of brawn and a bit of mustard on your plate, you will be joining my Dorset friend John Randall in a chorus of "they'm lovely!"

Family pressures have prevented me from ever managing to boil a pig's head at home, but I did once manage to cook a pair of ears without their noticing. My taste for pig's ears was somewhat tempered after the Romanian experience when, at the pig-killing, a fresh slice was taken from the pig's ear no more than minutes after it had died. This was then eaten raw, with salt. But not by me. I spat mine out in disgust.

I discovered a recipe which poached the pig's ears first in water, onion, salt, pepper and bayleaf, for about a couple of hours. The ears are then allowed to cool in their own stock, which turns to jelly. Once they are cool they are warmed slightly to melt the jelly and then coated with mustard, breadcrumbs and molten butter, and then cooked in the oven for ten minutes, till the crumbs are crisp. Sorry, but they are still disgusting. It is the vein of white muscle fibre that is sandwiched between the rather rubbery cooked skin that makes the whole thing too repulsive for words. In my opinion, the ears are best left on the head and allowed to impart their alleged subtlety to a fine brawn which is an infinitely more digestible delicacy.

But to discover things to do with pigs of which you would never have dreamed, we must return to Eastern Europe where contemporary cookbooks deal with pig knuckles, trotters and brain. Knuckles and trotters can be handled in two ways. Firstly, they should be cured, like a ham, in salt, saltpetre and water for up to six days and then washed to remove any excess salt. They are then poached and simmered till the meat is tender. Half way through the cooking can be added mixed vegetables of your choice – I would opt for onion, leek, parsnip or turnip – and to this add coriander, allspice and bayleaf. When all is cooked, the knuckles and trotters can be served with pureed peas (mushy peas to us) and horse-radish sauce.

For those of iron constitution, the *Polish Cookbook* by Zofia Czerny offers us "Pork Tongues in Dough" You should scrub the tongue, removing the salivary glands and rinse. Cook the tongue in water, vinegar and onion spiced with allspice and bayleaf until it is half-cooked and then remove the thick skin from the tongue and continue cooking till very tender. When cooked and cooled, cut the tongue into half inch slices.

Make a batter of egg, flour and water, blend with salt and oil. When you are ready to eat the tongue, dips slices of the tongue into the batter and quickly fry in hot fat till brown. Best served with raw vegetable salad.

Do you want to go for the big one? The ultimate recipe to dull the digestion of any Westerner who prefers his food pre-packed and beautified and fresh from the supermarket? I suggest Pork-Brain Cutlets, again from Poland. As pigs' brains are quite small, you will need one pork brain per portion:

> Rinse the brains, remove the membranes and boil several times (sic), allow to cool. Divide the cooled brains in two, sprinkle with pepper and dip each part in flour, egg and breadcrumbs. Heat some fat in a pan and add breaded brains and brown gently on both sides. Serve with potatoes, raw salad, carrots and peas, or spinach.

I offer these recipes not to shock or revolt you but rather to impress upon you the spirit in which other cultures approach the entire pig, and to show how far removed we have become from the natural sources of our food. We simply do not want to think of brains, or tongues, or trotters. A juicy joint cut so as to be no longer reminiscent of any part of the original animal is fine, but we must not get too close to the truth. It is too scary.

I hope this book has made you less nervous. I would not wish it to end on a down note, for it has been a celebration of one of man's best friends, and so let us end in grand celebratory style with a Stuffed Roast Pig fit for a banquet.

Old Polish Traditions in the Kitchen and at the Table tells us

> Five to six weeks old suckling pigs are the tastiest. After killing the pig and scalding it with boiling water, shave off the bristles very thoroughly with a sharp knife. Just to be sure, the shaven pig may be singed over with a spirit flame (particularly the ears). After shaving the pig, cover it with very cold water for an hour, then draw, setting aside the lungs, liver and heart. Then wash the pig in cold

water, dry with a clean linen cloth and salt one hour before roasting. After this time, stuff with the chosen farce, arranged on a large oven-pan with the back side up and the legs tucked under and roast in a well-heated oven. During roasting, the pig is often basted with a feather dipped alternately in beer and in melted butter. This make the pig brown nicely and evenly to an orange-brown colour and the skin becomes deliciously crisp.

Stuffing number 1: Simmer in butter the liver, lungs and heart of the pig with 20 oz. of boned veal and with a finely chopped onion and vegetables (parsely and celeriac root, 1 carrot). Remove the liver earlier, as soon as it becomes tender. Grind the lungs, liver and meat in a meat grinder. Cook 12 oz of pork fat and cut into small cubes when cooled. Soak 2 white rolls (grate the crust off) in milk and squeeze out well. Mix the ground meats, pork fat and rolls thoroughly with 2 raw eggs and the sauce in which the meat has simmered. Salt to taste and season with ground nutmeg and freshly ground pepper.

Number 2: this farce with raisins and almonds, also has a characteristic Polish note and it is perhaps for this reason that it is particularly good for stuffing an Easter pig, as it contrasts in flavour with the other meats.

Simmer the liver and lungs in 1 oz butter, adding some water, until the meat browns slightly. Next, grind in a meat grinder along with 3 white rolls that have been soaked in milk and squeezed out well.

Cream 3 oz butter until light and fluffy, adding 3 raw egg yolks while beating; add the ground meat with rolls, salt to taste, add 1 teaspoon of sugar, season scantily with pepper and a pinch of nutmeg. Mix well, add 6 oz of scalded raisins and 4 oz blanched almonds sliced into thin strips. Combine lightly with very stiffly beaten 4 egg whites and stuff the pig at once. Place the cooled roast pig on a dish, decorate with curly kale or myrtle sprigs and in its mouth place either a coloured Easter egg or a slice of horseradish or an intensely yellow lemon.

Now, with the whole hog at the very centre of the table, raise a glass to it. Give thanks for all the fine foods the pig can give us, praise the pig for the intelligent, docile creature that she is. Let us thank her for her versatility both in life and in death. And let us vow from hence forwards that we shall treat her with proper respect and dignity and, by making the very best of all the foods she gives us, ensure she will not have lived in vain.

The pig has lived only to eat, he eats only to die...He eats everything his gluttonous snout touches, he will be eaten completely.. he eats all the time, he will be eaten all the time.. The pig is nothing but an enormous dish which walks while waiting to be served . . . In a sort of photograph of his future destiny, everything announces that he will be eaten, but eaten in such a fashion that there will remain of him not the smallest bone, not a hair, not an atom.

Lettres Gourmandes: Charles Monselet, 1874

APPENDIX

I would not wish to select what I would consider to be a "winner" from any of the shops, farms and curers that I visited. They were all excellent and I would happily sit down to a plateful of ham from any of them. Each caters for a slightly different taste and pocket and I can only recommend you try them all!

I have listed them in the order in which they appear in the book.

F. E. Neave & Son (David Allen), 21 Cross Green, Debenham, Suffolk
Tel: 01728 860240

Richard Woodall Lane End Waberthwaite, nr. Millom, Cumbria LA 19 5YJ
Tel: 01229 717237

Ray Buckle 116 Roberttown Lane, Roberttown, West Yorkshire WF15 7LT
Tel: 01924 402594

Sutherlands of Eldon (Helen Sutherland and Sam Olive), Upper Eldon Farm, Kings Somborne, Hampshire, SO20 6QN Tel: 01794 368158

Denhay Farms Broadoak, Bridport, Dorset DT6 5NP Tel: 01308 422770

Sandridge Farmhouse Bacon (Roger Keen), Sandridge Farm, Bromham, Chippenham, Wilts SN15 2JL Tel: 01380 850304

Barrow Boar (Nigel Dauncey), Fosters Farm, South Barrow, nr. Yeovil
BA22 7LN   Tel: 01963 440315

Zissler's (Paul Zissler), 104 Bondgate, Darlington DL3 7LB
Tel: 01325 462590

If you are considering curing your own hams or bacon, and smoking it too, the most comprehsive selection of curing ingredients, smokers and other bits and pieces can be obtained from:

Home Farm Sausage Company (Don Bateman), Bramble Cottage, Field Lane, Hempnall, Norfolk NR15 2PB Tel: 01508 498302

One of the recurring problems I have found in dealing with butchers, slaughtermen and curers is one of language and so I reproduce here a list of technical terms which were published in the Ministry of Agriculture's booklet, *Home Curing of Hams and Bacon*. It would be dreadful if you were to mistake your brawner for your bussen, and end up with a pile of henge!

DESCRIPTION	COMMON NAME
KINDS OF PIG	
castrated young male	*hog, barrow, cut pig*
fattening pigs	
8 - 16 weeks	*slips*
16 weeks	*strong slips* (market term)
16 weeks when in	
yards for feeding	*stores*
maiden female	*gilt, yelt, yilt, hilt, spinder(?)*
castrated boar	*stag, brawner, seg, ste*
female after first litter weaned	*sow*
thriftless small pig in litter	*Dolly, Anthony, Sharger, Runt*
young pig	*spriggin, hogget*
thriftless pig	*dillon, cad, rutling, ritling, greck*
male pig, uncastrated	*bar, boar, bran, hog*
ruptured pig	*broken pig, bussen, bust*
unweaned pigling	*sucker, suckling, sucking*
weaned pig	*gummer, gunner, runner, weaner*
BONES	
backbone, vertebral column	*chine*
portion of half of pelvic	
girdle attached to a leg	*aitch bone, H bone, leech bone*
ribs, those at head end	*spare ribs*
shoulder blade	*blade bone*
portion of pelvic girdle	
attached to backbone	*oyster*

CUTS

A number of cuts consist essentially of bones with a small amount of meat or fat attached to them. Usually they are given the same name as the bones, but should not be confused with them.

hind leg cut from carcass before curing	*ham*
ditto wellcut round the aitch bone	*long cut ham*
ditto cut close to end of femur	*short cut ham*
hind leg cut off of Wiltshire cut side	
after curing	*gammon*
foreleg cut from the side like a ham	*shoulder ham, picnic ham,*
	fore, gammon spring
front part of Wiltshire cut side cut	
just behind elbow	*fore-end*
chine bone with 1 or 2 inches of meat	

and fat on either side	*chine*
lean meat attached to ribs	*spare rib*
lean meat attached to half of back bone in region of loin	*griskin*
side from which a straight cut ham has been removed	*spencer*
side from which a round cut ham has been removed	*jacket*
middle part of Wiltshire cut side	*middle*
lower part of middle	*streak, belly*
jowl, including lower jaw	*chap, chaw, chapper*
ditto cured and smoked	*Bath chap*
face, excluding lower jaw	*eyepiece, cheek*
feet	*trotters, pettitoes*
skin	*swarth*
fresh shoulder	*hand of pork*
spare rib	*short bones*

FATS

carcass fat over back and loin	*back fat*
fat lining the abdominal wall and running up round the kidneys	*flare or flair, leaf, flead, flick, body fat, brack*
fatty membrane surrounding stomach	*caul, veil, kell, kurtzer*
fat included in the mesentery	*mesenteric fat, mudgeon, midgeon, mudgerum, midrum, gut fat, crow, frill.*

OFFALS

intestines	*bellies (not to be confused with the belly cut), innards, pots, puddings.*
small intestines	*casings, tharms*
large intestines	*chitterlings, nedlings, netlings, notlings*
oesophagus	*gullet*
trachea	*windpipe*
lungs	*lights or lites*
spleen	*milt, melt, long-life (Lincs)*
stomach	*maybag, maw, nightcap*
connective tissue after rendering lard	*skretchings, scribbings, greaves, graves, kribbens, brousles*
liver, heart, spleen, gullet fat, gut fat and occasionally trimmings, and the tongue	*pigs fry, henge, inmeats*
lungs, heart, liver, trachea, oesophagus	*pluck, race, haslet*

EQUIPMENT
curing tub with lid	*salter*
shallow trough of stoneware	*thrall*
shallow wooden trough on legs	*standard, trundle, salter*
oval tub on legs	*coolin, turner*
bundles of straw for singeing	*boltings, patterns*
stretcher for carrying carcass	*cratch*

CONDITION OF BACON
Rancid	*reasty, rusty*
Mitey	*minty*

BIBLIOGRAPHY

Farm and Field, Richard Jefferies
Ask The Fellows Who Cut The Hay, G. Ewart Evans
The Homesteaders Handbook, Compiled By Martin Lawrence,
The Pioneering Pig, Norman Blake,
Garden And Allotment Pig Keeping, Walter Brett
The Cookery Of England, Elisabeth Ayrton
English Recipes And Others, Sheila Hutchins
Russian Food, Jean Redwood
Old Polish Traditions in the Kitchen and at the Table, Maria Lemnis and Henryk
    Vitry
Cottage Economy, William Cobbett
Handy Guide For Pork Butchers, Thomas B Finney
Home Curing Of Hams And Bacon, Bulletin No 127 of The Ministry Of
    Agriculture and Fisheries, 1949
Land Of My Cradle Days, Martin Morrissey
A Yeoman Farmer's Son, H. St G. Cramp
The Dalesman: A Celebration of Fifty Years
Good Neighbours, Walter Rose